THE ONE PER CENT ADVANTAGE

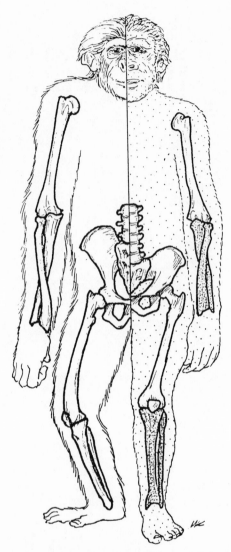

Comparison of *Pan paniscus* with a reconstruction of *Australopithecus* using information from Hadar and Sterkfontein. Note the similarities in overall size and in the lengths of the lower limbs and the differences in the somewhat shorter upper limb in *Australopithecus* and in its modifications for bipedalism in the pelvis and foot. From Adrienne Zihlman, University of California, Santa Cruz.

JOHN & MARY GRIBBIN

THE ONE PER CENT ADVANTAGE

THE SOCIOBIOLOGY OF BEING HUMAN

Basil Blackwell

British Library Cataloguing in Publication Data

Gribbin, John
The one percent advantage.
1. Human behavior
I. Title   II. Gribbin, Mary
150   BF131
ISBN 0-631-16004-3

Library of Congress Cataloging in Publication Data

Gribbin, John R.
The one per cent advantage/John and Mary Gribbin.
p.   cm.
Bibliography: p.
Includes index.
ISBN 0-631-16004-3
1. Sociobiology.   I. Gribbin, Mary,   II. Title.   III. Title: One
percent advantage.   IV. Title: 1 percent advantage.
GN365.9.G75 1988   87-29359
304.5-dc19

Typeset in 12 on 13pt Bembo
by Joshua Associates Limited, Oxford
Printed in the
United States of America

The average human protein is more than 99 percent identical in amino acid sequence to its chimpanzee homolog . . . the nucleic acid sequence difference of human and chimpanzee DNA is about 1.1 percent.

Mary-Claire King and A. C. Wilson, *Science*, 1 April 1975

Life is what happens to you,
when you are busy making other plans

John Lennon, *Beautiful Boy*

CONTENTS

Acknowledgements   ix

Introduction   BEING HUMAN   1

Part I Who are People?

1 A RATHER UNUSUAL AFRICAN APE   5
   A Prince among Chimps   6
   Evolution, Molecules and Man   8
   A Basis for Selection   16
   The Living Link   20

2 MARATHON MAN   25
   The Genetic Base   26
   From Conception to Birth   29
   The Peter Pan Process   34
   From Birth to Adolescence   37
   The Naked Ape   45
   The Quality of Humanity   47
   Marathon Man – or Aquatic Woman?   51

3 WORDS AND MUSIC   57
   First Words   58
   Wired for Sound   60
   Broca's Brains   62
   Evolutionary Implications   65
   The Right-handed Ape   67
   The Strategy of Left and Right   71
   When Left is Right   75
   The Food of Love   80
   Childhood's End   85

Part II The Rules of the Game

4 IN PRAISE OF SOCIOBIOLOGY   89
  What is Sociobiology?   90
  Sociobiology Today   94
  Intelligence and Evolution   98
  The Intelligence Test   100
  Sociobiology, Heredity, and Intelligence   105

5 PEOPLE ARE QUITE NICE, REALLY   109
  The Group Selection Fallacy   111
  Darwin up to Date   114
  The Birds and the Bees   116
  The Altruistic Ape   122

Part III The Games People Play

6 SEX GAMES   131
  Sources of Sex   133
  Sex Roles and Sex Ratios   136
  Why Monogamy?   141
  Choosing a Mate   149
  Men, Women and the Future   154

7 THE GENERATION GAME   159
  The Successful Smile   160
  Forming the Bond   162
  The Battle of the Generations   163
  Old Fogies and Young Tearaways   167
  The Parenting Puzzle   169

8 WAR GAMES   175
  Cowardly Lions   176
  Tribes and Nations   178
  The Prisoner's Dilemma   182
  The Safety of Tit-for-Tat   185

Appendix   ARE APES DESCENDED FROM MAN?   189

Notes   200

Bibliography   203

Index   209

ACKNOWLEDGEMENTS

This is very much a family book, describing relatively new and important ideas about an area of science where the interest of one of the authors, long fascinated by the topic of human evolution, and those of the other author, equally intrigued by the psychology of people today, overlap. It seems, as you will discover if you read on, that there are sound scientific reasons why we should have engaged in the collaborative venture; people are very good at cooperating with one another to the mutual benefit of all concerned. That explanation, however, does not detract from the pleasure we have gained by working together on the book. And there are four other people who will benefit far less from the project than we have, but were still generous in their help and encouragement.

First, we thank Professor Edward O. Wilson, of Harvard University, for reading all of the text in draft and for his encourgement that we were indeed on the right track, at a time when we needed a boost to encourage us to keep our noses at the word processors. Yoko Ono Lennon kindly gave permission for the lines from John Lennon's song *Beautiful Boy* to appear as an epigraph. And our own two beautiful boys made significant contributions. Having one parent immersed in preparing a book is bad enough, having both lost in the same task cannot have been any fun at all; but Jonathan helped to keep the home running by cooking and providing tea and sympathy, while Ben assisted directly by typing drafts of some sections into our Apple computers. We hope they will still think it all worthwhile when they see the finished product.

Finally, the Appendix is based on an article by Jeremy Cherfas and John Gribbin that first appeared in *New Scientist*, 3 September 1981; the theme is developed in their book *The Monkey Puzzle*. Adaptations of some of the other themes developed here were broadcast by John Gribbin in a BBC Radio Four series, 'Being Human', in 1987; these benefited from discussions with the producer, Michael Bright.

INTRODUCTION
BEING HUMAN

What does it mean to be human? Most people, asked that question, respond with thoughts about the things that make us special – achievements in art or science, the trappings of so-called civilization that mark us out from the other species that inhabit the Earth. The idea that humankind is special is so deeply ingrained that even people who have training that ought to have opened their eyes can fall prey to the cosy assumption of human superiority. A little while ago, for example, we offered a news report about a recent investigation of human behaviour to a friend who works on a scientific magazine. The work depended on treating human beings according to exactly the same rules of evolutionary behaviour as red deer, or elephant seals – a quite defensible thing to do, in the context (if you want to know more, you will find the story in chapter 6). Our friend, who shall remain nameless, responded immediately, and instinctively, 'I can't use this,' he said. 'You can't treat people the same way as you treat animals.'

It took some time to persuade him just how much of a *non sequitur* this remark was. We hope that in this book we shall persuade you (as we eventually persuaded him) that, indeed, the *only* way to get a deep understanding of human behaviour is to apply to humankind exactly those rules that prove so successful in explaining the way other animals behave.

Being human simply means being one variety of animal on planet Earth. Our similarities with other species, with whom we share a great deal of our genetic inheritance, turn out to be more remarkable than the differences. The title of our book reflects this, but still does not go far enough to satisfy all the colleagues with whom we discussed our ideas while writing it. There is, impeccable modern chemical techniques show, only one per cent difference between the genetic material, the DNA, of a human being and a chimpanzee. Small wonder, in that case, that human beings conform very closely to the patterns of behaviour of other animals. We are human chauvinist enough ourselves to refer to the 'one per cent *advantage*' that the differences give us over chimpanzees and other apes, even though the more pedantic of our colleagues urged us to refer only to the one per cent *difference*.

In terms of ultimate truth, our colleagues may be right. Who can say, objectively, whether people are better than chimpanzees? But from our own point of view, it is the one per cent difference in our DNA that has made human beings out of African apes, and, to human beings, being human is clearly a good thing. In this book we shall show you what it really means to be human, and how our lives continue to be moulded and influenced by our animal inheritance. Where better to start than with the evidence that we are, indeed, only one per cent human and 99 per cent ape?

PART I
WHO ARE PEOPLE?

1

A RATHER UNUSUAL AFRICAN APE

In 1928 a young American zoologist called Harold Coolidge was in Europe visiting various museums to gather data for what was to become a definitive study and classification of the different types of gorilla. Late one afternoon in the Musée Royale de l'Afrique Centrale in Tervuran, Belgium, he casually picked up from a storage tray a small skull that seemed, at first sight, to belong to a young chimpanzee. To his amazement, Coolidge noticed that the bones of the skull were totally fused, set in the permanent adult state, with no room for further growth. The skull was not that of a young chimpanzee, but that of an adult with a much smaller head than any recognized chimp. In adjoining trays, the young researcher found four similar skulls, and eagerly took note of their measurements, to report to the scientific world at large at some future date. By then it was closing time at the museum, and on the way out Coolidge described his findings to the museum director, Dr Henri Schouteden. He then went off to continue his gorilla study.

Two weeks later, a more senior researcher, Dr Ernst Schwarz, came by the Tervuran museum, and the director mentioned Coolidge's discovery to him. 'In a flash', as Coolidge recalled more than 50 years later, 'Schwarz grabbed a pencil and paper, measured one small skull, wrote up a brief description [and] asked Schouteden to have his brief account printed without delay.'[1] Schwarz's paper appeared in print in April 1929; Coolidge had been scooped by an unscrupulous rival. But this only fired his enthusiasm to find out more about these strange chimpanzees that lived only in the great sweep of jungle embraced by the bend of the Congo river (on its southern side), in what was then the Belgian Congo.

A Prince among Chimps

With his gorilla study completed, Coolidge turned his attention to chimpanzees. He carried out a comprehensive survey of museum specimens, revising the classifications with the same care that he had applied to the gorilla study, and reached the conclusion that this hitherto unrecognized 'pygmy' chimpanzee must be a species in its own right, *Pan paniscus*, and not simply a subgrouping of the familiar common chimp, *Pan troglodytes*. To many zoologists, this seemed an interesting, but not particularly dramatic, discovery, After all, in the 1930s the jungles of the Congo still harboured many species that had not been identified and classified by man. What was one type of chimp more or less? But Coolidge was convinced that he had stumbled upon something of major importance to our understanding, not just of chimpanzees, but of ourselves.

Ironically, Coolidge had already met a living pygmy chimpanzee, without realizing at the time the significance of the occasion. This was 'Prince Chim', a chimp in the possession of the great American primatologist Robert Yerkes. Yerkes bought the chimp from a dealer in New York in August 1923, and was informed that he came from somewhere in the eastern part of the Belgian Congo. Although Prince Chim died of pneumonia in July 1924, so that he was under scientific observation for less than a year, he made such a dramatic impression on Yerkes that he became the subject of a book, *Almost Human*.[2] As the title suggests, Prince Chim was really something special. In the book, Yerkes describes the differences between Chim and the common chimpanzees with which he was already familiar. Chim's bold, alert intelligence made him a leader among chimps, and he readily imitated human activities (including, on one occasion shaking hands with a young student, Harold Coolidge) and learned rapidly from his experiences. By chimpanzee standards, said Yerkes in his book 'Prince Chim seems to have been an intellectual genius.'

In the 1920s and 1930s, no less than today, primatologists were intensely interested in the closest living relations of our own species,

Homo sapiens. Charles Darwin, in his classic *The Descent of Man* had speculated that the common ancestor of man and the hairy apes (the chimpanzee and the gorilla) probably lived in Africa, and it was generally accepted by scientists that the chimp and gorilla species are indeed our nearest relations. We all recognize this instinctively, without the need for scientific study – that is what makes the chimpanzee enclosure at the zoo so fascinating. Man, chimp and gorilla, it seemed, must have shared a common ancestor, a 'missing link', not so far back in the evolutionary past. But what did that ancestral ape look like? A particularly intelligent type of chimp with an unusual ability for walking upright seemed, to Coolidge at least, to be an even closer relation to us than the common chimp is. When his detailed chimpanzee study was published in 1933, Coolidge presented the case for *Pan paniscus* as a species in its own right and went further with the speculation that the pygmy chimp 'may approach more closely to the common ancestor of chimpanzees and man than does any living chimpanzee'[3] – not so much a missing link as a *living* link with our past.

You might have expected such a dramatic claim to make waves not just in the world of science but in the wider world outside. Almost any new idea about human ancestry seems to provoke fierce arguments for and against. But Coolige's hypothesis was the exception. The idea was presented in the scientific literature, its existence was acknowledged, and then it sank, almost without trace, to be largely ignored for another half century. When the relationship between man and the pygmy chimp began to make scientific headlines again in the late 1970s and early 1980s, it was thanks to a completely different line of attack on the puzzles of evolution. Instead of looking at animals from the outside, or at the fossil bones of extinct species, and trying to assess relationships on the basis of morphology, from the 1960s onward a growing band of researchers had been looking at the molecules which make up the tissues of living animals today.

Modern molecular biology techniques make it possible to compare, directly, the proteins in a small sample of blood or tissue from one animal with the equivalent proteins in a sample from a member of another species. It is even possible, now, to compare directly the DNA molecules, the molecules of life, from one species with those of

another. These techniques provide a direct measure of the relationships between living species, Obviously, if the samples are from two
members of the same species, they are essentially identical; samples
from two different species differ by appropriate amounts, and the
greater the difference the more distant relations the two species must
be. In evolutionary terms, the greater the difference the longer it is
since they shared a common ancestor.

When these techniques are applied to samples from our own species
and the other primates, they show that the chimpanzees and gorillas
are indeed, as Darwin guessed, our nearest relations – such close
cousins, in fact, that less than two per cent of the genetic material, the
DNA, in your body is different from the DNA in a chimp or gorilla
chosen at random. The pygmy chimp is indeed slightly more closely
related to us than even the common chimp is (although, of course, the
two types of chimp are even more closely related to each other than
either is to man), and compared with the pygmy chimp we are, in
round terms, only one per cent human and 99 per cent ape. This in
turn means that the common ancestor we share with chimps and
gorillas walked on Earth, or swung from the trees, very recently indeed,
only about five million years ago. These dramatic discoveries have
swung the spotlight firmly back on *Pan paniscus* in the past few years;
but before we bring the story of the pygmy chimp up to date, we
should at least outline the new molecular studies and put them in their
evolutionary perspective. (What follows is only the bare bones of the
story. John Gribbin has told the full story of DNA and its significance
in evolution in *In Search of the Double Helix*; with Jeremy Cherfas, he has
put mankind in an evolutionary perspective in *The Monkey Puzzle*.)

EVOLUTION, MOLECULES AND MAN

DNA is the stuff of life. The initials stand for deoxyribose nucleic acid,
the chemical name for the material which carries the hereditary
message from one generation to the next, and which is decoded by the
living cells to act as a blueprint for the construction of the chemical
compounds required to keep the new individual alive and to provide
for its healthy growth. Molecules for DNA are generally very long
chains made up of many smaller chemical subunits. The basic

structure of each chain, its backbone, is a repeating sequence of alternating phosphate groups and sugars – the name of the sugar unit, deoxyribose, is what gives DNA its name. Every phosphate group is the same as every other one; each sugar is identical with all the other sugar units in the chain. But the crucial importance of DNA for life is that each of the sugar units in the chain has one of four other types of molecule attached to it, sticking out from the chain. These molecules are called bases; the four types of base found in DNA are adenine (A), cytosine (C), guanine (G) and thymine (T). It is this string of bases along a DNA molecule that spells out the genetic 'message'.

All the rest is just superstructure. What matters is the string of bases. In the same way, the message in this book is contained in a sequence of letters. It does not really matter what kind of paper the book is made of, or what colour ink the letters are printed in – indeed, when we were writing the book the letters appeared first on the screens of our word processors, not printed on paper at all, and these symbols, or their equivalent, have since been processed electronically several times before reaching the pages of the book you now hold. But always their message is the same. So, for our present purposes, we can ignore the sugars and phosphates and think of a DNA chain as simply a string of letters in the genetic four-letter alphabet, AGCCATGTCATT . . . and so on. 'And so on', in fact, with a vengeance. For if all the DNA in one normal cell of your own body could be extracted and laid out in a line it would stretch over a distance of 175 cm, even though each molecule is less than a millionth of a centimetre thick. If all the DNA in all the cells in your body could be unravelled and laid out end to end, it would stretch for between 10 and 20 *billion* kilometres, but a length of DNA sufficent to reach from the Earth to the Sun would weigh no more than half a gram. The way DNA is fitted inside the cell is a masterpiece of packaging, a story which we can only touch on briefly here. The DNA in one cell is not a single, continuous molecule, but is packaged in several separate chains, called chromosomes, in which the DNA is coiled and twisted back upon itself to make thick, short rods of genetic material. In all human cells there are 46 chromosomes, so the average 'molecule' of human DNA would be 3.8 cm long if an average chromosome rod could be unfolded and stretched out. (In fact, the coiling of DNA into supercoils within the chromosome makes each tiny rod so compact that all 46, laid end to end, would only cover a length of 0.2 mm. Some chromosomes are much bigger than others – in human sells, the largest are 25 times as big as the smallest – so the 'average' used in the calculation is purely a hypothetical example.) Such a length of DNA includes 100 million sugars, each with its own base attached – a message amounting to 50 million letters of the genetic alphabet, since the sugars and their attached bases come in pairs. In all, the 46 human chromosomes contain some 2500 million base pairs, a coded message which, if typed out in print of the same size as the letters on this page, would cover roughly a million pages like the one you are now reading. Even allowing for the limitations of a four-letter alphabet compared with the 26 letters of the English alphabet, this is still an impresssively long message which can carry a great deal of information. The structure of DNA ensures both that this whole message can be faithfully copied and passed on to offspring (new cells or new individuals) and that *parts* of the message can be translated, as required, and the information they contain used in the processes that maintain life.

Take cell reproduction first. We have talked about DNA, so far, in terms of a single, long molecule, but, of course, DNA usually comes in the form of paired molecules, twining around each other to form the famous double helix. In the double helix, the two DNA chains are linked by chemical bonds which hold the bases on the two molecules together. The bases only pair up in two specific ways – A always matches up with T, and C always matches up with G. Every G on one strand is 'mirrored' by a C on the other; every A sees its reflection in the form of a T. The two strands of the double helix are, in a sense, mirror images. And if the double helix is unravelled, each strand can rebuild its partner by collecting the raw materials from the chemical soup inside the cell in such a way that the bridges between the two halves of the new helices are made up solely of AT and CG bonds.

This happens every time a living cell copies itself and splits into two, a normal feature of growth. Each DNA molecule untwists, and the half-helices gather on opposite sides of the cell. Each builds itself a new partner, with the aid of protein molecules in the cell, and finally the cell divides into two identical daughter cells, each with an exact copy of all the original DNA double helices.

Now how about the role of DNA as the genetic blueprint? In this case, something a little more subtle than wholesale copying is required. Each chromosome, with its 50 million letter message of instructions, carries far more information than is likely to be needed by the living cell at any one time. But within each chromosome there are subunits, distinct regions of DNA that have their own 'start' and 'stop' markers, that each code for one particular chemical process. Such a stretch of DNA is called a gene, and the message between the start and stop markers is the code which tells the cell how to manufacture one type of protein molecule. Proteins provide both the structure of a body and the 'engineers' that keep it working. Your body is largely made of proteins, and the haemoglobin molecules that carry oxygen around in your blood (to take just one example) are also protein molecules. When a region of DNA – a gene – is active, the appropriate stretch of the double helix in one chromosome is untwisted, and the genetic message is 'read' by chemical workers inside the cell and transcribed temporarily into a short stretch of a molecule known as RNA (like DNA but with a different sugar in its backbone). Finally, the RNA message is used to construct the necessary protein molecule. The RNA is then broken up and its components are re-used in reading off another DNA message. This process is going on all the time in all the cells of your body, keeping everything ticking over just the way it ought to. But there is an even more important, and still only poorly understood, role played by the DNA and its protein engineers.

How did your body get to be the way it is? It started from a single cell, in which a sperm carrying chromosomes from your father met and fused with an egg carrying chromosomes from your mother. Those 46 chromosomes we mentioned before are actually 23 pairs, and in each pair there is what seems to be a duplication of effort. In one pair of chromosomes, for example, each of the long DNA molecules might carry within itself a short stretch – a gene – that determines eye colour. On one chromosome, the instruction might read 'blue eyes'; on the other, 'brown eyes'. In that particular case, the body which carries those genes will have brown eyes. (Like much of this description of the workings of DNA, the assumption that there is 'a gene' for eye colour is a simplification. Probably several genes, perhaps from different chromosomes, contribute to determine eye colour. But the simplified

11

version helps to make our point.) Brown-eye genes are dominant over blue-eye genes. One version of the gene – one allele – seems to be wasted. But, when the body that contains those chromosomes manufactures gametes (egg cells or sperm), new chromosomes are manufactured in a complicated (and poorly understood) process which involves cutting up the paired chromosomes and mixing the genetic material from one partner with that of the other to make two new chromosomes. Just 23 single, new chromosomes then go into each gamete, and when two gametes fuse the full complement of 23 *pairs* is restored. One member of each pair comes from the mother, and one from the father. But each chromosome in each pair is a mixture of genes that have been cut out of chromosomes inherited from *both* parents of the person who 'donated' that gamete and pasted together to form a new combination of genes. Where the gene for blue eyes might previously have sat next to a gene for blond hair, taking another simplistic and hypothetical example, it might now find itself sitting alongside a gene for red hair. And where before it was dominated by a brown-eye gene on the partner chromosome, perhaps in this new body it finds another blue-eye gene (strictly speaking, another blue-eye allele) on the partner chromosome, and with no opposition the character for blue eyes is indeed expressed in the body in which the genes reside. It is the inheritance of genetic material from two distinct parents, plus all this cutting and pasting of genes (usually referred to as recombination) that ensures the enormous variety of individual human beings, and sexually reproducing individuals. Apart from identical twins, or triplets or whatever, produced when one fertilized egg divides and copies all its 46 chromosomes, no two human beings who ever walked the Earth have had identical DNA blueprints.

Still, how does a unique fertilized egg, a single cell, develop into a fully functioning human adult – or indeed into the adult form of any other species? The marvel of biological development of the adult form from a single cell is the greatest unsolved problem in biology today. It is easy to talk in generalities, and to describe the outlines of what must be going on inside individual cells during development, but we are still very far from understanding how those general principles are put into practice. Nevertheless, the general principles themselves provide crucial insight into how we can be so different from the chimpanzees even though we share 99 per cent of our DNA with chimps. Clearly, during the growth of a complex body from a single cell different portions of the DNA message are activated and used at different times in different cells. Something – we do not know exactly what – 'tells' a certain group of cells that they are destined to become, say, the liver. In those cells, only the portions of the DNA message that describe the functioning of liver cells are switched on; although each cell carries the whole 46 chromosome genetic blueprint, it does not 'care' whether or not it inhabits a body with blue eyes or red hair or whatever. It functions simply as an efficient liver cell. This involves operating in accordance with just a few pages from one volume of the 'encyclopaedia' that is represented by all of the human DNA in a cell. How does the liver cell know which pages to read, and to ignore the rest? This still largely unsolved puzzle provides one of the most exciting areas of research in modern molecular biology, holding out the possibility that answers to these questions may provide means to control the cell's mechanisms and, for example, prevent the occurrence of cancer.

This skill is not, of course, unique to liver cells. Elsewhere, another group of cells is 'told' to become a leg. The cells grow and extend in one direction to become the embryonic limb, laying down muscle tissue, blood vessels and bone as required. Growth continues after birth until the body is adult and then it stops, presumably in response to another message contained within the DNA blueprint. You can think of other examples for yourself. What matters from our present perspective is that clearly there must be mechanisms within the cells that decide which parts of the DNA message are to be activated, and when they are to be active. But there is nothing to provide these instructions except the DNA blueprint itself. So there must be genes which control the behaviour of other genes, turning them on and off, speeding up or slowing down their activity, and generally regulating the processes of growth and development. Since the DNA blueprint is contained in every living cell, these regulatory genes are also present in every living cell, and can modify its behaviour. And this is the clue to the differences between human beings and other apes.

Perhaps an analogy will help to make our point clear. Suppose you are baking a cake to a recipe which reads, in part, 'take half a pound of flour and two ounces of butter'. You can take exactly the same words

13

and rearrange them so that the instructions read 'take half a pound of butter and two ounces of flour'. But the cake you bake according to the second recipe will be very different from the one made by following the original instructions. Or suppose the instructions read 'add half a pint of water and simmer for 20 minutes'. The outcome would be very different if the instruction being obeyed were 'simmer for 20 minutes and add half a pint of water'. Again, these are identical words in a slightly different order. The stretch of DNA which 'tells' a human body to 'grow a leg' may be identical with the stretch of DNA which 'tells' a chimp body to 'grow a leg'. But if the message is switched on at a different time during development, and for a different *length* of time, the two legs produced will be very different from one another. A small difference in a control gene can produce a big difference in the body that is the end product of development (the phenotype).

Again, we are not suggesting that there *is* such a specific, simple instruction in human or chimp DNA, nor that two equivalent instructions really are identical in the DNA of the two species, but there must be instructions rather like this in our DNA and that of our cousins, and the principle is the same.

Now, at last, we can see the significance of the findings from molecular biology that 99 per cent of our genetic material is the same as that of the chimp and gorilla. The molecules which are compared to find the genetic distance between two species include many types of protein, as well as the DNA itself, and always the message is broadly the same. All the proteins in a human body are made from combinations of some of 20 chemical units called amino acids. The haemoglobin molecule, for example, is made of chains of amino acids folded and twisted together in such a way that they provide an oxygen carrier. The order of the amino acids along each protein chain is determined by the gene that describes the construction of that protein – the whole business of transcribing the DNA message simply translated a chain of bases (AGACGTGTTCA and so on) into a chain of amino acids. The haemoglobin can function perfectly well if one or two of the amino acids in the chain are swapped for others, and when the proteins from different species are compared this is just the kind of difference that is found. Chimpanzee or gorilla haemoglobin is very, very similar to our own. It carries oxygen just as efficiently. But there are one or two minor, insignificant substitutions in the amino acid chain, and these must reflect equivalent minor, insignificant substitutions among the bases of the DNA double helix that codes for this protein.

The same story is found for many proteins. When it comes to the DNA itself, it is not yet possible to map out the entire base sequence of even one human chromosome – all 50 million pairs of letters – and compare it with the equivalent chimp chromosome, but it is possible to carry out a piece of chemical trickery whereby the paired strands of *all* the genetic material in a sample of human cells can be separated and mixed with similarly separated strands of DNA from the cells of chimps or gorillas or, indeed, other species). The separated strands try to pair up again, but where a strand of human DNA combines with a strand of, say, chimp DNA to form a double helix, the new helix is not held together as strongly as a normal strand from either species. Where the bases on the two strands fail to match up with their proper partners on the other strand (A with T and C with G), there are weaknesses. The strength of the bonding between such hybrid strands of DNA can be measured, and this provides a direct measure of the number of weak links. We do not know exactly *which* bases are different in the two DNA strands, but we can tell, very accurately, *how many* bases are different. It is this hybridization technique which says that there is a 'genetic distance' of about 1.2 per cent between ourselves and the chimpanzees – out of every ten million bases on a hypothetical 'average' human chromosome, only 120,000 will differ from the bases on the equivalent chimp chromosome. (In the interests of scrupulous accuracy, we should mention two things. First, the chimp actually has 48 chromosomes (24 pairs) to our 46 (23 pairs); molecular studies show that one specific human pair is the same as two chimp pairs fused together. Secondly, we are talking here about differences in *the DNA that codes for proteins*. There is a lot of DNA in the chromosomes that does not *seem* to code for anything useful, and this intriguing discovery is the subject of a later chapter. The important point now is that just one per cent of the genes that code for proteins in you body are different from the genes that code for protein in the body of a chimpanzee.) These small differences ensure, among other things, that the proteins manufactured from the chimp's DNA blueprint are very similar to, but not quite identical with, the equivalent proteins manufactured in accordance with the human DNA blueprint. And if some of those different bases on each of the 46 chromosomes lie in the control genes that determine development and growth from a single cell, then it is very easy to see how the body that develops is in one case a small, hairy ape and in the other case a tall, upright, naked ape.

How, though, did these differences arise?

A Basis for Selection

Differences in the DNA of different species, and differences in the DNA of different members of the same species, are the basis of evolution by natural selection. Bodies – phenotypes – that are well suited to their environmental surroundings will do well, and will pass on copies of their successful genes to many descendants. Phenotypes that are less well adapted will have fewer offspring, and over the generations the better fitted genes will dominate. Evolution requires two things. There must indeed by selection of the most suited organisms, with reproduction so that they pass on their successful genes, but this carries with it the implication that there is a variety to select from. That variety arises from changes in the DNA content of living cells, imperfections in the copying process.

Now, we are not, in this book, going to address the big questions in evolution, such as the origin of life itself, or the origins of major groups like the mammals, or why a man is different from a fish. We are concerned with the way things are on Earth *today*, and what the best current ideas on evolution and genetics can tell us about ourselves, as human beings. There is, in fact, a lively debate among the experts today on how major evolutionary changes occur, and whether these changes are gradual or relatively sudden ('sudden', in evolutionary terms, meaning something that happens in the course of only a few million years). The minor differences in DNA that distinguish human beings from other apes do not come into this debate. They are clearly a set of small adaptations which have occurred simply through the routine copying, and occasionally *mis*copying, of genetic material.

No copying process is perfect, and although the cell mechanisms that copy DNA are pretty good, they too have their imperfections. Mistakes that occur during the everyday process of cell division responsible for growth are of no great significance here, because they have no effect on future generations. But mistakes that occur during the cell divisions that use recombination to produce new chromosomes for the sex cells that lead to the development of new individuals clearly are important. They can result in the production of completely new genes, variations which have never existed before. And those new genes can then be tested against the rest when, and if, the chromosome in which they sit becomes expressed in a new body.

Copying errors can happen in several ways. One letter of the genetic code might be miscopied, with a T, say, going into a stretch of DNA where there ought to be a G. But this is a pretty boring and trivial kind of mutation. Much more interesting things happen during the wholesale cutting and re-splicing of chromosomes that goes on during recombination. A chink of chromosome might get copied and then inserted into its new home the wrong way round, so that the message reads backwards – this is called an inversion – or a chunk might be cut out altogether, with the daughter chromosome being spliced together across the gap. If that happens, the spare piece of DNA may become a new chromosome in its own right, and new chromosomes can also be generated when part of an old one is copied twice. Then there are changes like those that have happened in at least one pair of our own genes, where two chromosomes that used to be separate have been spliced together by mistake. (As well as this fusing of chromosomes, there are six inversions which distinguish human chromosomes from chimp chromosomes – and no other differences that are distinguishable without resorting to the DNA hybridization technique.) Anything you can imagine happening to a chromosome during the process of recombination surely has happened, and will happen again. The genome is much more flexible than it appears at first sight. But most of these mutations will have little effect on the body they inhabit. For one thing, a distorted version of a gene, a rogue allele, will usually be paired up with a normal allele inherited from the body's other parent, and the rogue will never get expressed. Then again, small, subtle changes will have no major influence on the body – the fact that the haemoglobin in the blood of a gorilla has one amino acid, out of a chain of more than 100 such acids, different from the haemoglobin in our blood does not make it any less, or any more, efficient at carrying oxygen. Just occasionally, however, the new form of a chromosome will code for the production of proteins which makes the body it inhabits more effective. That body will do well, and will pass on its new genotype to its offspring, who will do well in turn and so spread the new gene throughout the 'gene pool' of succeeding generations of that species.

Why, though, did three families of ape - ourselves, the chimps and the gorillas - begin to follow different evolutionary paths some five million years ago? Almost certainly, this kind of speciation is a result of different groups of an original parent species becoming isolated from one another, either through geography or through different lifestyles. An isolated group on an island is the obvious example, and it was the distinction between closely related species of bird on the Galapagos Islands that led Charles Darwin to his theory of evolution. But an equivalent change might occur if, for example, a climatic shift caused an extensive forest region to begin to dry out, so that the forest shrank and became surrounded by grassy plains. For a species of tree-dwelling ape in that forest, there would be two possible ways, at least, of adapting to such a change. The individuals, or family groups, that were still in the middle of the forest would succeed best as tree-climbers and leaf-eaters. But their relations living on the edge of the forest might need to adapt to a different diet, and would need to be able to move out over the plains. There would be different selection pressures on the two groups, and as a result they would begin to diverge.

How rapidly would the process take place? Molecular biologists can now measure these evolutionary changes and set up a kind of evolutionary clock, or calendar, to put them in perspective. Closely related species today clearly share a common ancestor - the horse and the zebra provide an obvious example. If this ancestral form can be identified in fossil remains, it is sometimes possible to determine reasonably accurately when it was that the two forms began to go their separate ways. Armed with this information, the molecular biologists can go back to their studies of proteins and DNA from the living descendants of those fossils, and compare one species with another. Originally, in the ancestor, all the DNA and proteins were essentially the same. As the two 'new' species have evolved, the molecular clocks inside each of them have ticked up a variety of mutational changes that make the two species what they are today. So the molecular studies can determine, directly by measurements in the laboratory, how many changes have occurred in a particular protein in a particular span of time, or, indeed, how many changes have occurred in the DNA itself in that time. The astonishing discovery that came out of these tests in the 1960s and 1970s is that although each type of molecule investigated (each protein) changes at its own rate, the same protein (haemoglobin, for example) changes at roughly the same rate throughout the generations of many different species.

There is no particular reason to expect this, but it is found to be so by studying the proteins of many living species today, including our own. The number of differences in the protein chains of haemoglobin between one species and another gives you a rough indication of how long it is since those two species shared a common ancestor. A similar study of another protein, called cytochrome-c, will give you the same date read off from a different calendar, and in most cases the date can be read off from several such calendars. To give you a feel for the changes involved, in cytochrome-c change accumulates at a rate of one per cent of the protein chain every 20 million years, while haemoglobin shows a change of one per cent in every six million years, equivalent to a change of one single amino acid every three and a half million years.

For closely related species, such as ourselves and the chimps, the date can also be read off from direct comparisons of DNA. Each individual calendar is only a rough guide, but when they all give essentially the same date then the molecular biologists know for sure that they are dealing with a fundamental evolutionary truth. And all of these techniques imply that there was a three-way split between man, chimp and gorilla about five million years ago, while the DNA hybridization technique, in particular, says that humans and chimpanzees shared a common ancestry for a short time after the gorilla line split off. (Details of this revolutionary development in biology can be found in *The Monkey Puzzle*.)

This discovery of a molecular clock has been one of the greatest breakthroughs in evolutionary understanding since the time of Darwin himself, and we have described the work in a little detail because it is so new and exciting. But, strictly speaking, it is not directly relevant to our main theme. We are concerned here not with the grand sweep of evolution and the origin of species, but with the way animals, especially human animals, behave today. Clearly, the behaviour of animals depends on the coded DNA message in their genes. We should expect our own behaviour to depend, at least to some extent, on our genetic inheritance as well. But we might have expected to find our genome so different from that of 'lesser' animals that we would not expect to gain much insight into our behaviour by studying them. Far from it. Whether or not you accept the timing of the molecular clock which says that *Pan paniscus* and *Homo sapiens* shared a common ancestor as recently as four or five million years ago (indeed, *whether or not you accept the theory of evolution at all*), there is no escaping the fact that 99 per cent of our genetic material is *the same* as the genetic material of the pygmy chimpanzee. And it is that fact alone which establishes, beyond a shadow of a doubt, that the best way to understand what it means to be human is to look at what it means to be an animal on Earth today. Our genetic inheritance is *very* similar to that of some species, and broadly related to that of a wider circle of more distant relations. If we understand how genes work to determine the behaviour of animals in general, then we shall understand 99 per cent of our own inheritance, and we shall be equipped to identify the one per cent that makes us special. But before we begin this search for ourselves, we should take one last look at the pygmy chimp that represents the nearest living thing on Earth today to our own immediate ancestors. As recently as December 1984, writing in the journal *Science*,[4] reporter Roger Lewin commented that the outcome of DNA studies which showed man and chimp to have shared a common ancestry for a short time after the gorilla line split off 'is unexpected'. He would not have been so surprised at this molecular evidence, perhaps, if he had been familiar with the work of Adrienne Zihlman and her colleagues, first published back in 1978, which argued both from the molecular evidence and from physiognomy the case for just such a relationship.

THE LIVING LINK

The fundamental feature that distinguishes our own species, physically, from its closest relations is that we walk upright, on two legs. The shift from four locomotive limbs to two would have been easiest to achieve in a small, light animal. The nearest living creature to a small, lightly built 'four-legged person' is, of course, the chimpanzee, and for this reason alone in 1968 Vincent Sarich, of the University of California, had already singled out the chimp as the 'model' that should be used by anyone trying to reconstruct the appearance of mankind's immediate ancestor. Sarich was, and is, one of the pioneers of the molecular clock techniques, and was involved at about that time in studies which showed, for the first time, that man and chimp had indeed shared a common ancestor as recently as five million years ago. Following in Sarich's footsteps, and working with him in the 1970s, Adrienne Zihlman discovered Coolidge's 1933 paper on *Pan paniscus*, and carried out a study of the body build and skeleton of the pygmy chimp in comparison with *Homo sapiens* and the common chimpanzee. By 1978, this work led to the publication of a paper in *Nature* with the clearest possible title: 'Pygmy chimpanzees as a possible prototype for the common ancestor of humans, chimpanzees and gorillas'.[5]

The paper hardly took the scientific world by storm. In 1978 the palaeoanthropologists still did not take the molecular clock seriously. But, not long after that was published, Donald Johanson and Tim White published their description of a previously unknown fossil species which walked in East Africa about three million years ago and which is widely believed to represent our own immediate ancestor. This is the famous fossil 'Lucy', whose story was told by Johanson, with Maitland Edey, in their popular book of the same name. Zihlman and her colleagues claimed that the immediate human ancestor probably looked like a pygmy chimp: now, fossils representing the immediate human ancestor had turned up. The obvious question was, how did those fossil remains compare with the bones of present day *Pan paniscus*? Zihlman has carried out a now famous reconstruction in which the bones of Lucy and the bones of a pygmy chimp, drawn to the same scale, are juxtaposed alongside each other to give the appearance of a composite creature. The result is so striking that we have used it as the frontispiece of our book. And the conclusion, in the words of Zihlman and Jerry Lowenstein at a symposium held in 1980, was inescapable: 'the earliest known hominids at 3.5 million years may have

21

been only one step away from a small ape like the living *Pan paniscus*'.[6] (It is only the *skull* of the pygmy chimp that is small compared with *troglodytes*; the rest of the skeleton is roughly the same size. So the common chimp in your neighbourhood zoo will give you a fair idea of the size, although not the detailed bone structure, of both *paniscus* and Lucy.)

Since 1980, as more data have accumulated and traditional palaeontologists have come to accept the evidence of the molecular clock, the case has strengthened still further. In 1982, a symposium on the pygmy chimpanzee was held, in honour of Harold Coolidge, in Altanta, Georgia, The proceedings were published in book form in 1984[7] and may have come just in time, for the pygmy chimp, now the subject of intense scrutiny by anthropologists and evolutionary biologists, is almost on the verge of extinction.

Until recently, the only observations available of the behaviour of pygmy chimps were those of a dozen or so individuals kept, like Prince Chim, in captivity. In the early 1980s, Randall Susman, of the State University of New York, and a small team of researchers spent 18 months studying *Pan paniscus* in the wild, in the Lomako Forest of Zaire, the pygmy chimp's last surviving natural home; similar studies have been carried out by Japanese primatologists. Among the remarkable features which the pygmy chimps share with *Homo sapiens*, but not with the other African apes, are a very long period of sexual receptivity in femals, with no clearly defined 'mating season' or short-lived regular periods of sexual activity, and a tendency, at least some of the time, to mate front-to-front. Mixed groups of males and females are much more important in pygmy chimp society than the all-male bands which are important in the social organization of common chimps. And, of course, there is the pygmy chimp's already well-known ability to walk upright with more ease than his *Pan troglodytes* cousin.

Studies of captive pygmy chimps continue. One of these, Kanzi, seems to be a true modern counterpart to Prince Chim. He lives at the Yerkes Primate Research Center in Atlanta (named in honour of Prince Chim's one-time owner), where E. S. Savage-Rumbaugh works with him. In the published version of the 1982 symposium, she describes how Kanzi frequently combines gestures with his vocalization, pointing towards things he is eager to show his teacher; no *Pan troglodytes* can do this. He also leads his teachers by the hand to get them to go where he wants, something he was never taught to do and which no common chimp has ever been seen doing. All in all, the behaviour of pygmy chimpanzees, and their response to training in communicating with people using symbols, is much more like the behaviour of human infants than the behaviour of comparably trained common chimps is. 'Each individual who has worked with both species in our lab', says Savage-Rumbaugh, 'is repeatedly surprised by their communicative behaviour and their comprehension of complex social contexts that are vastly different from anything seen among *Pan troglodytes*'.[8]

The case that the pygmy chimpanzee is our closest living relative, and that it may well retain many of the features of our common ancestor, a living link with Lucy and our past, is overwhelming. In the words of Roger Lewin, '*Homo sapiens* is really just a rather unusual African ape'.[9] We could, clearly, learn a lot about our past, and probably not a little about ourselves, by studying *Pan paniscus* in his natural habit. But, unfortunately for *Pan paniscus*, one of the features that makes us unusual among apes is our ability and apparent inclination to wipe other species from the face of the Earth. The forests in the Lomako area are being cut back to make way for coffee plantations, and the relatively small numbers of surviving pygmy chimps are today hunted both for their meat (considered something of a delicacy) and to provide bones used in local religious practices, as well as to provide for the pet trade, zoos, and, ironically, scientific laboratories and primate study centres like the one in Atlanta. A live chimpanzee can fetch four or five times as much, on the black market, as a plantation worker earns in a month.

Efforts are now being made to inform the local population of the real value of *Pan paniscus*, as Kabongo Ka Mubalamata of the Institut de Recherche Scientifique in Bukavu, Zaire, told the Atlanta meeting.[10] In addition, the Research Institute is urging protection measures involving the creation of a reserve for the pygmy chimpanzees and is stepping up efforts against the black market trade and illegal hunting. But these efforts may be too little, too late; there remains a very real risk that the pygmy chimp may become extinct just at the time when it is being recognized as our nearest relative. That would be a sad reflection on human nature; in the rest of this book, we intend to reflect on human nature in general, and also on how we can used our one per cent advantage to overcome our sometimes inappropriate genetic programming.

2

Marathon Man

What distinguishes us, physically, from the hairy apes that are such close relations to ourselves? Leaving aside the behaviour that makes us 'civilized', the most striking feature of *Homo sapiens* in relation to other mammals is that our babies are the most helpless and immature at birth, and need the longest period of protection while they develop into independent individuals. Childhood, for us, is lengthened, in comparison with that of the infant gorilla or chimpanzee, at both ends of the scale. Our babies are born early, in an unfinished state – if our bodies followed the same relationship between average size and duration of pregnancy as all other primates do, then human pregnancy would last for at least a year, perhaps longer, instead of for nine months. And, even allowing for this extra period of helplessness, our infants seem to stay infants for longer than their hairy cousins.

All of this may be related to another striking characteristic of our species. Like the relationship between body size and length of gestation, there is a very clear relationship between body size and lifespan which applies to all other primates. According to this, the average lifespan of a human being 'ought' to be about 30 years' in fact, in the developed world, very many people can expect to live well beyond the biblical 'three score years and ten', barring accidents. For comparison, whereas the human gestation period of 266 days is just over one per cent of our 70 year lifespan, the gorilla's 257 day pregnancy corresponds to just over 3.5 per cent of its 20 year life and for a chimp the figures are very similar. Looking at more distant relations to *Homo sapiens*, the lion has a gestation period of 108 days, some 2.5 per cent of its lifespan, while the elephant's impressive 624 day pregnancy (almost two years!) corresponds to almost five per cent of its life.

Our whole lives, not just our infant stages, are stretched out compared with those of our nearest relations. In terms of total lifespan, as well as time taken for development, mankind is the long-distance runner of the primates, designed for staying power rather than sprinting through life. The analogy is even more apt than it may seem at first sight, since it also turns out, as we shall see, that many of the adaptations which stretch the human lifespan also make mankind literally well suited to long-distance running. But more of that in its place.

A long period of development and the ability to learn new tricks – an ability extending right into old age – are the key features of *Homo sapiens*. So, before we can look at the way that an understanding of the genetic inheritance we share with those close relations can provide an understanding of human patterns of behaviour, it is wise to look in more detail at this long, slow process of development, from conception to the adult state. It all builds, of course, from the genetic base mentioned in passing in chapter 1.

THE GENETIC BASE

Since we are concerned with the development and abilities of just one species out of the millions on planet Earth today, it is as well to be sure just what we mean by the term 'species'. There are several ways of defining a species, but from our present perspective the one that matters is a group of animals that mate with one another to produce fertile offspring. Dogs and bitches mate to produce puppies which grow up to be dogs and bitches; men and women come together to produce offspring which grow up and have children in their turn. Dogs and bitches are members of a single species, and men and women are members of another species. But dogs do not mate with, say, budgerigars; the two are members of different species. And, drawing the line very carefully between close relations, although a he-ass and a mare can mate to produce offspring – a mule – the mule itself is infertile and can have no offspring of its own. So the horse and the ass are different, albeit closely related, species. Any healthy adult male human being could, in principle, mate with any healthy female human being of child-bearing age to produce healthy, fertile children, so every person on Earth, regardless of size, shape or colour, is a member of one species, *Homo sapiens*.

There is, of course, a great deal of variation between individual members of a particular species, including our own. Individuals pass on at least some aspects of their own individuality (size, hair colour, length of index finger, and so on) to their own children. In the animal world at large the success of individuals, specifically their ability to live long enough to find a mate and reproduce, depends on how well they fit into the environment around them. If some aspect of a particular individual body – a phenotype – helps that body to find food and live to become a parent, then that characteristic has a good chance of being passed on to the next generation. These are the three keys to Darwinian evolution – variation from one individual to another, the inheritance of characteristics passed on from parent to offspring, and the selection of successful characteristics by environmental pressures. When Darwin talked of 'survival of the fittest', he did not mean the most athletic individuals; he meant, as we hope we have made clear, the ones that fit best into their surroundings, making good use of the available food, coping with hazards (such as predators and the weather), and finding a mate. The fit of the pieces of a jigsaw puzzle, rather than the image of a super fit Olympic champion, gives you a better idea of what Darwin meant.

Very recently, in terms of the timescale of evolution, mankind has begun to change the environment to suit himself, instead of adapting, through natural selection, to fit in with the existing environment. This involves a new stage in the story of life on Earth, but it only began to happen a few tens of thousands of years ago, when our ancestors began to use tools and make fire. There has not been time for this new factor to play a significant part in determining our genetic makeup, although it has, of course, enabled us to spread across the world and to increase the total population of human beings on our planet dramatically.

That genetic inheritance, remember, is passed on from generation to generation in the form of 23 pairs of chromosomes, one member of each pair coming from the mother of a new human being and the other from its father. Genes, strung out along the chromosomes, therefore come in pairs, and within those pairs an individual gene may be either dominant or recessive with respect to its partner, so that in an individual person only one of the genes is necessarily expressed in the phenotype. And, as a further complication, most of the characteristics of a body as complex as our own bodies are determined by a combination of several genes interacting with one another. Size is an obvious example. Children do not grow up to be exactly as tall as either parent. This is partly, of course, because genes only provide a *potential* for growth; the actual size of an adult human being depends also on environmental factors – for example, on how much food the child gets to eat – working in conjunction with the genetic package the child has inherited from its parents. More of this later – we would not be so foolish as to claim that genes alone determine even the physical features of an individual, but it is simplest to consider genetic inheritance first and then to look at the interactions between genes and environment. Even the genetics are complicated enough, when so many characteristics are controlled by many genes working together.

Such characteristics are said to be polygenetic, that is, under the influence of two or more genes. This is why it is impossible to predict exactly what a new baby will look like, or how it will grow to adulthood, simply by looking at its parents. If the mother has blue eyes and the father brown, the offspring will not have one eye of each colour, but probably either brown or blue, and perhaps even green, depending on how the recessive and dominant genes match up in its chromosomes. If mother is tall while father is short, the chances are that the offspring will be in between; but he or she might very well either end up taller than either parent or be shorter than both of them, even without any environmental influence on growth, because of the polygenetic influence of many genes working together to determine the phenotype. Of course, we may say that a boy 'has his father's nose', or that a girl's eyes are 'just like her grandfather's'; even within your own family you can see the inheritability of characteristics. But you cannot predict in advance that one, or any, of your own children will have 'your nose' or 'their grandmother's hair'. Control genes guide our development, from conception to maturity, and ensure that we develop as members of *Homo sapiens*, not as horses or pigs. Within that broad definition of a species, though, there is plenty of room to manœuvre.

FROM CONCEPTION TO BIRTH

The individual human being that we recognize with our senses is a phenotype, the bodily expression of some combination of genes working together. But it is the unique genotype that decides how that individual person has been put together, and that new genotype is determined at the moment of conception, when a single sperm carrying a half-set of chromosomes from the father penetrates a single egg containing a half-set of chromosomes from the mother. Once this happens, a complex train of processes is set into operation. The surface of the egg immediately changes to prevent penetration by any other sperm, while the nucleus of the sperm, containing its load of genetic material, moves to the centre of the egg and combines with the genetic material it finds there. The egg is now a single cell, called a zygote, carrying a full load of 23 pairs of chromosomes, but less than one-hundredth of a millimetre in diameter.

Just over a day later (about 30 hours after fertilization), the single cell divides to form two cells; after 60 hours, the two cells each divide to make four cells in all; and after three days the four divide to produce a ball of eight cells. All the while, the little ball of cells has been moving down the Fallopian tube towards the uterus. By the sixth day it has arrived, in the form of a hollow ball made up of a few hundred cells; this is called the blastocyst. From now on different cells have very different roles to play, and develop and differentiate from one another accordingly. As the blastocyst burrows into the lining of the uterus and implants itself, the outer layer of cells begins a series of changes that will lead to the development of a placenta, to draw nourishment from the mother's bloodstream and to pass it on to the developing embryo, while taking waste products from the embryo, through an umbilical cord, and delivering them to the mother's bloodstream for excretion or reprocessing. The embryo itself starts off as a small cluster of cells inside the blastocyst. The term 'embryo' is used once implantation has been completed, by the end of the second week after fertilization. After eight weeks (two months) the embryo has developed to the point where it is given yet another name, the foetus. The embryo begins to develop at one end of the hollow sphere of cells, confined within its own inner chamber, a chamber that will become a cavity (the amniotic cavity) filled with fluid in which the developing embyro can grow and be protected from harm.

Most of the blastocyst, apart from this initially tiny chamber, is empty – it is, in fact, an evolutionary left-over from the days when our ancestors laid eggs filled with yolk to nourish the developing embryo. The blastocyst 'surrounds' a yolk sac that is no longer there, discarded in the course of evolution. This is an interesting sidelight on how evolution works. When, through mutations, an improvement on an existing pattern is thrown up, the beneficiaries, the new individuals, still have to carry with them the baggage of their inheritance. Evolution, if we anthropomorphize wildly, cannot say 'Aha, I think an animal that brings its young forth alive will be more successful than one that lays eggs', and start from scratch to design a perfect mammal. Instead, a mammal evolves by a series of small changes in the 'blueprint' that describes an egg-laying reptile. Richard Dawkins, in particular, has expressed reservations about this use of the term 'blueprint' to describe the information passed on to succeeding generations in the genetic code. He says, rightly, that the information is more like that contained in a recipe, which says 'take the following ingredients and cook them up together', rather than a genuine engineering blueprint, which specifies in detail what the end product of a construction will be. The environment – the cooking – is also relevant to development. We take his point, but we are happy to live with the more colloquial usage of the term, equally respectably enshrined in the dictionary, meaning a general guide that influences subsequent developments. It is, perhaps, a small step for a yolky egg that has already 'learned' to implant itself inside the mother and draw nourishment from her bloodstream to 'learn' to discard the yolk that its ancestors needed, but, judging from the evidence of the development of every human baby, it is a bigger step to change the whole pattern of development of the cells surrounding the yolk to stop them forming a sphere where the yolk used to be. Anyway, the hollow sphere is soon overtaken in size by the developing amniotic cavity and the embryo it contains, and shrivels away to nothing, just as it would if it contained yolk that was being used to feed the foetus.

The mass of cells that will become a new human being starts out as a flat disc. Within a week of conception, the disc begins to differentiate into different kinds of cells – first two distinct layers, and then three. One layer contains the kind of cells that will develop into the nervous system, hair, skin and nails; on the opposite side of the sandwich is a layer of cells that are destined to form the internal organs, digestive tract, lungs, and so on. In the middle are the cells that develop to form muscle, the skeleton, and the circulatory system. Exactly the same pattern of three cell layers develops at this stage in all animals; it is something we all inherit from a very, very remote ancestor. And the control genes that determine how the cells develop are clearly very much in control right from these earliest stages of development, as they must be if a new adult is to be produced and reproduce itself in its turn.

At two weeks, the now rapidly developing embryo is a mass of cells about 1.5 mm across. Now, development of this tiny speck of incipient humanity begins to mould and shape the embryo into something recognizably human. First, a grove forms across the top of the embryonic disc, and the edges of the groove close up to make a hollow tube. The front of the tube grows, thickening and expanding to form the brain; the back part of the tube will become the spinal cord. Three weeks after conception, the embryo is 2.3 mm long, and is beginning to develop internal organs, such as the gut. Another tube forms, and begins to pulsate by about day 24; it will become the heart, pumping 100 000 times a day or more for as long as the new human being lives. By the end of the first month, this simple tube has developed into a four-chambered pump; buds that will become the arms and legs have started to form; and the rudiments of the eyes, ears, nose and mouth are apparent on the embryo. It is still only a little over 5 mm long, and the mother who carries the embryo may not even be aware yet that she is pregnant.

By the time she is, probably, certain that she is pregnant, two months after conception, the embryo has completed all of the important stages in laying the foundations for the development of its internal organs and its ultimate outward appearance. From then on,

31

the important process is growth, and the development of the individual parts of the body to take up their work when the baby is born; differentiation, the process of creating different kinds of organ and body material out of an initially uniform mass of cells, is largely complete. The foetus, as it is now called, has a skeleton, arms and hands with fingers, legs and feet with toes, internal organs, and a very large head in proportion to its body, complete with the beginnings of eyes, ears and all the rest. And all of this clearly defined within a miniature person in the making – a foetus that is about 2.5 cm long and weighs less than a single aspirin tablet, about 1 g, just under one-thirtieth of an ounce.

At about this time, just before it qualifies as a foetus, another interesting feature of the embryo reaches its largest size. This is its tail, another reminder of our ancestry. Also during the second month, features resembling the gill slits of a fish appear in the neck region of the embryo, only to develop later into structures of the face and neck. And over a period of several weeks, from the end of the first month into the third month of its life, the embryo/foetus goes through a three-stage process of kidney development. First, it starts to form a type of kidney found in primitive fishes and eels, but this soon disappears and a second, more complex, version starts to develop. Even this kidney, though, also disappears before the third and final, most complex pair is formed and begins to carry out its function. These, and other features of the developing embryo, show how evolution is unable simply to discard outmoded designs. A great deal of the DNA in our chromosomes – perhaps the great majority of it – is never expressed at all in the phenotype. Some of this DNA is thought to be 'junk' spacer material or simply rubbish picked up through evolutionary time, but some may well be versions of old genes that used to be essential for our distant ancestors, genes that describe the construction and working of a tail, or gills, or a primitive kidney. Evolution proceeds not by cutting these old genes out and replacing them by new and better ones, but by developing more efficient genes ('more efficient' in terms of survival and reproduction of the phenotype) that override and suppress the old material. Although it is not as simple as saying that the developing embryo goes through all the stages of evolution as it develops, as biologists once thought, it is true that the sometimes strange looking cul-de-sacs of development do carry reminders of our evolutionary past.

All of that, though, is rapidly fading by the time the embryo becomes a foetus. The rudimentary tail, for example, disappears before birth in 94 per cent of cases, and even in the other six per cent it is concealed by the flesh at the base of the spine, detectable only as a skeletal appendage in X-ray photographs. During the third month, the foetus begins to move its arms and legs, and it also begins to develop sexual characteristics. As the sex organs form and develop, in a male foetus they release a hormone, androgen, which ensures that the body they reside in develops male characteristics. In a female foetus, of course, there is plenty of female hormone present in the blood circulating, via the placenta and umbilicus, from the mother, so there is no need for extra female hormone, oestrogen. The baby teeth are being laid down at this time, and the foetus can suck and swallow, frown or squint. By the end of the third month it is about 23 cm long, from the tip of its head to its buttocks, with its tiny legs legs folded up in front of it, and it weighs about 15 g, roughly half an ounce.

During the fourth and fifth months, the foetus begins to straighten out from its original curled up shape, and the developing organs move down the body cavity into their proper places. After about 4.5 months, the mother begins to feel the foetus move, and by the end of the sixth month a typical foetus will weigh about 1 kg (two pounds). By now, it is 30 cm long or more - roughly a foot - and very long and thin for its weight. A layer of fat is only just beginning to develop, and the lungs, for example, are not yet finished off; but if a six-month foetus is born prematurely it has a chance of surviving, with the aid of modern medical aids such as respirators.

The last three months of pregnancy finish the job off. The foetus fattens up, doubling in size in the last two months, and putting on weight at a rate of 30 g (an ounce) a day. At birth, it probably weighs about 3 or 4 kg, although there is a wide variation. The lungs have developed into working order, and the nervous system is refined to control breathing, heart beat, sucking and swallowing. On average, the baby will be born 266 days after conception, although in fact only three-quarters of all human births are within two weeks of the 'target' date. But although it can breathe, see, hear, suck, cry and wave its limbs about, it is still a very helpless creature with a head much larger in proportion to its body than that of an adult human being. That large head, and the brain it contains, is a key reason for the baby being born at all so soon.

THE PETER PAN PROCESS

Biology teachers, and textbooks, often close this stage of the story of human development with a throw-away remark along the lines of 'the genes have done most of their work by the time a baby is born'.[1] This is a striking way of getting across the important message that the genes responsible for the day-to-day running of your body – making sure there is haemoglobin in the blood, keeping the blood pumping around, producing the right mixture of stomach juices to digest your food, and so on – play a quite different role from the genes responsible for development. It is the development process that produces a distinctively human baby instead of a member of some other species, such as a chimp. DNA is sometimes referred to as the 'blueprint' which specifies a phenotype; extending that analogy, the genes responsible for development from conception to birth are at once blueprint, architect and construction engineers. Although some considerable physical development still takes place after birth, the genes that keep the body running during its adult life can then be likened to the janitors, cleaners and maintenance engineers that keep a great building running once it has been constructed. Without those genes performing effectively, the body will die. But without the genes that control development, there would be no living body for them to maintain in the first place.

The crucial differences that make us human instead of chimpanzee, the one per cent advantage we have over our cousin apes, almost certainly lies very largely in those genes that control development. As the example of the tiny difference between our haemoglobin and that of a gorilla shows, the actual running of the end product, the ape or human phenotype, is essentially the same in man, chimp and gorilla. Without doubt our large brain is a key feature of the difference between us and those other apes, and the way this has been linked, in evolution, with the production of babies several weeks earlier than they 'ought' to be born shows just how a small, subtle change in the development process can have big effects on the phenotype.

By and large, the bigger an animal is the bigger its brain has to be to control its body. People are pretty large mammals – among the primates, only gorillas are larger than us. So we ought to have big brains, perhaps weighing 100 g or so less than the brain of a gorilla. In fact, a typical human brain weighs about 1300 g, roughly twice that of a gorilla. Also, interestingly in view of the evidence that chimps are our very closest relations, the chimp, although much smaller than a gorilla, has a brain weighing almost as much as the gorilla's, about 600 g. We do not need to labour the evolutionary advantages of our large brains – intelligence, tool making, speech, philosophy, arts and science. We can see that under the right kind of environmental pressures increased brain size, in proportion to body weight, will make a species more successful, better 'fitted' to its environment. But there is immediately a problem here for our anthropomorphic image of evolution as a tinkerer who has to make do with the kind of biological systems that are available. There is a limit to how big the brain and head of a foetus can grow in the womb and still be capable of being born without its mother being killed in the process. Birth is difficult enough for human mothers as it is; if they carried their babies in the womb for another three months or more while they finished off to the standard of other primate infants at birth, it would be impossible.

So the evolutionary change which has led to human infants being born early is directly linked to the changes which have increased human brain size so dramatically. At birth, the human brain is one-quarter of its final size, and the skull is still soft, with large 'spots' where the bones have not yet met and fused, to allow for its continued growth. When a rhesus monkey is born, however, its brain is already two-thirds of its ultimate size. One year after birth, the brains of even our nearest relations, the chimp and gorilla, have reached 70 per cent of their mature weight; a human infant takes two years to reach the same landmark, so by this criterion we are born a full *year* 'too early'! But this central feature of human development at and after birth, the growth of the brain, is only part of the story of how humans fail to grow up like other apes – or perhaps we should say, how humans *succeed* in hanging on to youth.

Adult human beings share many features with infant apes. Our large brains are housed within a domed skull with a flat face, very much like that of the baby chimp or gorilla – or indeed baby kittens and puppies. Later on, though, all these species develop a distinctive adult shape to the head, with a more or less pronounced snout. We do not. The ratio of the length of our limbs to our bodies, as well as of the head to the body, is also more like that of an infant ape, or even an ape foetus, than that of an adult. Even our lack of prominently visible body hair, the appearance of the famous 'naked ape', is something that we share with the newborn chimp, or ape foetus, rather than the adult forms. In very many ways human development seems to be retarded, so that, leaving aside size, we resemble ape infants rather than ape adults. Like Peter Pan, we never grow up into the adult ape form, although many of us, of course, show traces of further development as we get more hairy with age.

Now this pattern of characteristics is quite common in evolution, sufficiently so for it to have a special name, neoteny, meaning 'holding on to youth'. It involves only a very small change in the control genes that mastermind development, and so it is a very easy mutation to occur. It has happened time and again throughout evolutionary history that a species has evolved into a neotenous form, never completing all the stages of development that its ancestors did, and then begun to evolve again along a slightly different path. The best example of neotenous process (apart from ourselves) perhaps comes from the Mexican axolotl, a creature rather like a giant tadpole but with four small limbs, that lives and breeds in water. An ordinary tadpole, of course, cannot breed until it has metamorphosed into a frog. Curiously, though, this sometimes also happens to the axolotl. Under the right circumstances it will metamorphose into an adult form, a salamander, and breed in the usual salamander or frog fashion. The axolotl is a neotenous salamander, an immature form that has 'learned' to live its life and reproduce without developing further. In this case, neoteny takes the form of switching off, essentially, the set of genes responsible for metamorphosis. Undoubtedly, it has also happened many times – probably even more often – that a neotenous mutation has occurred, but the resulting phenotype has been no better fitted to the environment than its parents, or the 'normal' descendants from its parents' generation, and so the new line has promptly died out. Variation *and selection* are both crucial to evolution.

In our case, the situation is less dramatic than in that of the axolotl. We simply develop more slowly, from infancy right through to adulthood and on to the ends of our lives. We are born 'unripe', as it were, take a long time to grow up, and live for much longer than we should. The Peter Pan ape indeed – a powerful piece of evolutionary magic, that can quite easily be explained in terms of a change in the workings of a fraction of one per cent of our DNA, just the small part of our genetic material that controls the rate of development. It is, of course, quite another matter to explain *why* this should have occurred. What were the environmental pressures which made having a larger brain, and all of the other features of a neotenous ape, an advantage for our ancestors in eastern Africa some five million years ago? Nobody knows for sure why intelligence should then have been placed at an evolutionary premium, although there are two good, front-running theories that are worth a mention. Before we come to them, though, let us complete the story of the slow development of a human being, from the cradle on, if not quite to the grave.

From Birth to Adolescence

By any objective criterion the newborn human baby is a nasty sight. Its head may have been squeezed into a distinct point by the process of birth, while its ears have undoubtedly been squashed flat against its skull. It arrives covered in a white protective coating that looks distinctly cheese-like, called vernix, and splotched with its mother's blood. Some are bald; others are covered in a layer of hair that, fortunately, does not persist for long. And yet people respond with tender affection to these nasty little creatures, looking after them with care and ensuring that the infant will survive and develop independence. Of course, this reaction is part of our own evolutionary programming. Human beings who did not like the look of new born babies and left them to die would be very unlikely to produce any offspring of their own that grew up to reproduce and pass on their genes. But people, and especially mothers, who for some reason respond favourably to a newborn infant will surely have lots of children and pass on whatever it is in their genetic makeup that makes them good mothers. Instincts, including the maternal instinct, arise, like physical features of the body, through the process of evolution by natural selection. And no more, or less, explanation than this is required to explain the basic set of instincts that the newborn human baby is supplied with.

The helplessness of our own offspring at birth can be easily seen by comparison with many other mammals. A newborn rhesus monkey can walk, after a fashion, and hold tight to its mother's fur within a few minutes of birth; to take an example from a more domesticated animal, a calf can stand and find its mother's udder almost immediately it is born. Even baby kittens, although born blind and helpless, develop independence in a matter of a few weeks, not the years it takes for a human infant to achieve any kind of independence from its parents or other adults.

The basic instincts of the new baby are connected with survival – obtaining food and acting in such a way that parents, and other adults, will respond in a protective fashion. The new infant can suck, cry, hear things, grip things and see things. The cry, thanks to evolution, has a powerful effect on the mother, who literally cannot bear, in most cases, to leave the infant unattended; very soon, the baby also develops a winning smile, to which we are conditioned, by evolution, to respond. A 'rooting' reflex makes the baby's head turn if its cheek is touched, in the direction of that cheek – an obvious advantage when it is trying to find a nipple to suck on, but something that can cause complications if an inexperienced mother tries to guide an infant's mouth towards her breast by gently pushing the *opposite* cheek.

The interaction between parents and newborn is, indeed, remarkable enough to merit a more detailed look later; but first we want to outline the rest of the development process.

During the first three months of its life, the baby develops from a scrawny, helpless creature with an overlarge head into something that has more human proportions, including a respectable covering of fat; it is alert and responsive to its environment, can hold its head up, and smiles beguilingly in social context. It begins to qualify as a human being in its own right instead of a foetus that emerged from the womb too early. Over the next year or so, it undergoes a dramatic physical development, from the early stages of learning to roll over and crawl to standing while holding on to furniture, standing alone, and eventually walking. There is a very broad range of 'normal' ages to achieve all of this – some infants, for example, can walk while holding on to furniture at little more than seven months, while others do not do this until they are 13 months old. But they all go through the same stages, in the same order. It is all part of the common genetic inheritance.

The shape of the developing infant also changes. In the womb, the head grew much more rapidly than the body, and at birth the head is still one-quarter of the total length of the infant. In the adult, the head is only one-tenth of the length of the body, because it has grown relatively slowly compared with the rest of the body. A two year old already looks much more 'grown up', for this reason, than a newborn baby does. The growth of abilities like standing and walking shows how internal processes, especially those connected with the workings of the brain and nervous system, are also developing into an adult state. But physical development, of the body or the nervous system, is, of course, not a particularly notable human activity. All healthy animals can walk about and find food and a mate; our cousins the pygmy chimpanzees do all this at a much younger age than we do, and they do a lot of things – such as climbing – rather better than we do. So we shall gloss over most of physical development here, taking it as read that people do learn to stand, walk, run, pick things up and carry them, and all the rest. What makes us special, thanks to that one per cent difference in our genetic material from that of the pygmy chimp, is our mental development, and that is what we shall concentrate on now.

Development of mental abilities is closely linked with the physical growth and development of the brain. From the quarter of adult weight that it has at birth, the infant's brain reaches 40 per cent of its ultimate weight by three months, half its adult weight at six months, and 75 per cent of its final weight shortly after the child is two years old. At the same time, the neurones within the brain – the 'wires and switches' of the biological computer – are developing. The neurones themselves get bigger, and the number of nerve connections joining them in a complex network steadily increases. Different regions of the brain develop at different times and at different rates – for example, the parts that control the legs and hands develop markedly between three months and a year after birth. But, once again, all of this physical development proceeds in line with the genetic blueprint, in the same sequence in all normal children. The control genes are still firmly in control. At this point, however, we have to grasp a thorny problem, the question of the balance between the role played by the genetic blueprint itself and environmental influences on the developing infant. We assume, of course, that the infant has enough to eat and is well looked after physically. Obviously a starving baby will not develop 'normally'. All of this discussion is about the role of less tangible, but no less real, influences.

This sometimes bitter argument is known as the 'nature/nurture' debate. There are, or have been, scientists who have argued that everything is determined by the genes, and that the environment (nurture) plays little part in development; at the other extreme there have been those who insist that nature (genetic inheritance) counts for very little except physiology, and that the key role in human development comes from the environment, conditioning the new human being to adopt certain characteristics that will remain important throughout life. As is usually the case with heated debates – not just scientific ones – the two extremes are unrepresentative. The truth lies somewhere in the grey area in between, and today most students of human development agree that both nature, the genetic blueprint, and nurture, the environment in which the baby develops, are important in determining the kind of human being the baby grows up to be. There is still debate about the exact balance between nature and nurture under various circumstances, but that need not concern us. What is important is that we take on board the concept of a *duality* of influences, from the genes and from the surroundings, because almost all the misunderstandings about what biologists mean by genetic programming of behaviour arise from a failure – sometimes wilful – by some people to understand that it is the interplay of the two effects that really matters. The one per cent advantage is there at birth – indeed, at conception – but only as a potential; how that potential is expressed depends on the baby's upbringing.

One example, widely quoted by experts on human development, should bring the point home. In the late 1950s, the American psychologist Wayne Dennis visited several orphanages in Iran. In some

40

of these understaffed institutions, although the children were physically cared for and kept clean and fed there were no resources to provide them with a normal family environment, and the overworked custodians of the infants carried out their duties like caretakers, providing little human contact. The babies spent virtually the entire first year of their lives in individual cots, and the sides of the cots were covered by cloths to prevent draughts, so they had nothing stimulating to look at. They were fed with bottles propped up in the cribs, not sitting on someone's knee, and they were picked up only to be washed and bathed, every two days.

Dennis found that the development of these infants was severely retarded. More than half of them could not sit unaided at more than a year old, whereas children reared in normal circumstances do this at nine months; more than 80 per cent of the three year olds in the establishments still could not walk alone, something the child in a normal environment almost invariably does before the age of two; and there were other, similar, signs of backward physical development. It looked as if the efficient development of the brains and nervous systems of the babies – all-important in developing these 'motor skills' – had been held back by the dullness of their lives.

So Dennis and a colleague set out to see whether the backwardness could be overcome by providing more stimulation. A group of 30 orphans, each one year old, in the Iranian institutions was tested to measure the stage reached in their development, and then divided into two equal groups. One group was left in the existing orphanage routine, as before. The other 15 babies were taken out of their cribs for an hour each day and propped up in a playroom with toys to play with. Within a month the second group showed a marked improvement in motor development compared with the first.

This is a classic example of the way in which stimulation from the surroundings *combines with* the basic programming laid down in human genes to produce the complete person. There are many recorded cases where children have simply stopped growing if they receive no affection from their parents – if one parent deserts and the child is neglected , or if the home is an unhappy one. Time and again doctors have found nothing wrong with such children except for their lack of physical development; and time and again psychologists and

41

doctors have watched in amazement as a change of environment (such as being adopted by loving foster parents) results in such a backward child suddenly putting on a growth spurt and catching up with its peers. So, whenever we talk, from now on, of the way in which an infant develops, remember two things. First, that although all normal children develop through the same stages in the same order, they do not all do so at the same rate – there is a wide variety of growth rates, both mental and physical, covered by the term 'normal'. Secondly, these processes of development can at the very least be hastened, or held back, depending on the child's home environment. With that in mind, we can make proper use of the insights into the development of knowledge and understanding in the infant – cognition – provided by the pioneering work of the Swiss researcher Jean Piaget.

Piaget lived from 1896 to 1980 and was the most influential developmental psychologist of modern times (although in fact he trained in biology and never obtained a psychology degree). Starting from observations of his own children as they grew up, Piaget developed the idea of four crucial stages in cognitive development. These were later broken down into more subtle substages, but such details need not worry us here. What matters is the basic idea that a child's capability to understand and interpret its surroundings develops in distinct stages, moving from one stage to the next only when the basic mechanisms of the brain have themselves developed to cope with the new demands placed upon it. In the first, 'sensorimotor', stage, from birth to two years, objects exist, for the infant, only when he or she has direct contact with them. A rattle that is dropped to the floor ceases to exist, as far at the infant mind is concerned; a person is part of the baby's world only when the baby can see, hear, touch or otherwise interact with them. 'Out of sight' literally means 'out of mind'. Then, at about two years of age (the exact timing, remember, can vary considerably from one individual to another), there is a relatively sudden change to a new stage in which the infant's perception is drastically different. The abruptness of the change, and its qualitative nature, are features of all Piagetian stages. In the second stage, 'pre-operational', which lasts very roughly until about the age of seven, a child can use language and can understand that objects exist when they are out of sight. A two or three year old, for example, will look for a toy that has rolled out of sight behind a chair. But to the pre-operational mind the world at large is still of very secondary importance compared with itself. The world revolves around the infant, so that children in this stage cannot see things from another person's point of view – if asked to draw a scene as if viewed from a certain perspective they will invariably draw it as they see it themselves. At the same time the developing mind in the pre-operational stage cannot reason with adult logic. Some children in this stage, for example, learn that living things move, and promptly decide that *anything* which moves must be alive, including a cloud, or a car.

Once again, the transition to the next stage is sudden and clearcut – we only say that it occurs *roughly* at the age of seven because the actual age varies from child to child. In each individual child, however, there is a very clear transition to the 'concrete operational' stage, when at last the child develops the ability to use logic in a more adult fashion, when he or she learns about the permanence of properties like number and mass, begins to be able to appreciate another person's point of view, and fully grasps the significance of relative sizes (A is bigger than B but smaller than C, so C is bigger than B, and so on). This is not to say that children in the pre-operational period are stupid. We recall an occasion when our older son was in this stage, and we visited a student deeply immersed in her work on developmental psychology. It happened that, following a party the night before, there were several bottles on the table. Eager to test her newly acquired knowledge of Piaget's theory, she lined some up in front of our son. Two half pint bottles stood alongside a pint one. 'Now,' she said, 'if I fill these two little bottles up with water and the big bottle up with water, will there be more in the big bottle or in both little ones together?' Unhesitatingly, the infant reached past her to a quart bottle looming large, to him, in the background. 'That one,' he said. He had no idea what the relative merits of two small bottles were compared with one larger bottle, but he could certainly identify the biggest bottle on the table.

Finally, some time after the age of 12 or so, the child passes into the 'formal operational' stage, and begins to put aside childish things and think like a man (or woman). Abstract reasoning and logic become possible, and he or she develops the ability to investigate all aspects of a problem systematically, eliminating unwanted or incorrect solutions to arrive at the required answer. It is only at this stage that the young human being can deal with hypothetical possibilities, and reason about 'might have beens'. So it is only in the formal operational stage that mathematics, poetry, science and art become a part of human life.

Education is, of course, an important feature of all human cultures. What education can achieve depends on the stage of development a child has reached, which follows the rules laid down in its genetic inheritance. Never let anyone tell you that 'genetics' has nothing to do with 'culture'. It is no coincidence that our educational systems, both in the developed world and in pre-industrial societies, are fitted to these stages of development. You cannot teach abstract mathematics or philosphy to a seven year old, so there is no point in trying. Many generations of experience established what could sensibly be achieved, long before Piaget came on the scene. What he did was to show how these abilities build, in hierarchical fashion, one upon the other, with each new stage using the groundwork provided by the stage(s) before. And again these stages in development of the mind are related to, and conditioned by, stages in the physical development of the brain itself. Unless the 'wiring' is right and ready, concrete operational behaviour, say, is impossible.

Language is such an important feature of being human that we shall deal with it in more detail later. Here it is appropriate to mention the work of the American linguist Noam Chomsky, who has revolution-ized our understanding of the way children learn to speak with his idea that the human mind is in some way 'pre-wired' for language, and that we are born with a special sensitivity to certain universal features of human grammar. We are programmed to be able to learn to speak, but the actual language we learn (English, Chinese or whatever) depends on the environment we are brought up in – and, in rare but genuine examples of human beings brought up in the wild, or kept in silent captivity, it turns out that the ability to learn language only persists for a specific time. If a child has not been given the correct stimulation to learn to speak – which is simply the opportunity to hear other people speaking – by the end of Piaget's pre-operational stage, at the very latest, then the child will never acquire language as we use it. Once a human being has acquired language, however, he or she has the ability to learn different languages at a later date. Song birds, for example, cannot do this. They seem to be programmed with a preference to learn songs from members of their own species, but can be persuaded, if kept apart from adults of their own species when young, to learn other songs instead, including songs no ancestor of theirs has ever learned. Once the pattern is established, though, such birds do not learn new songs when they are adult, even if introduced to members of their own species which sing the 'traditional' song.

This is a very powerful example of the links between nature and nurture, which highlights the single most important ability of human beings. We are able to learn new tricks. The calf, although able to stand and suck its mother's milk within minutes of birth, is so straight-jacketed by its genetic programming that it can never learn new tricks. A human being, on the other hand, is not programmed to fill a specific role but *to be able to learn new roles* (or new languages) as the need arises. That is what makes us special. Play is an important feature of the lives of the young of many species, for testing out their bodies and practising skills that will later be useful in hunting for food, or in hiding from predators. But humankind takes play acting seriously. We spend all our lives, not just our childhoods, playing out roles, at home, at work, and in our fantasies. It is all part of our unique ability to adapt and fit ourselves, not to one fixed ecological niche, but to whatever opportunites come to hand. And it begins as soon as we begin to develop into mature adult people, at puberty.

THE NAKED APE

Adolescence is a time of dramatic changes in both physical features and cognitive abilities. The physical side chiefly involves puberty, the time when, following a signal triggered by a part of the brain called the hypothalamus, the essentially sexless body of a child is transformed, in the space of a couple of years, into a form that is undeniably adult in the sense that it is capable of reproduction. Some of the growth, and much of the mental development, continues for several years after puberty has, by this strict definition, been completed. The onset of puberty can occur as early as eight years old in girls, or may not begin until (rarely in modern society) age 17; for most boys it begins later than for most girls, but obviously with such a range of variation some boys complete puberty before some girls of the same age begin this transformation. A reasonable, but arbitrary, definition for the end of adolescence is age 18, at which time most modern Western societies regard the individual as an adult, with adult responsibilities, such as the right to vote. Interestingly, the right to reproduce (that is, legal marriage) is often conferred even younger, at sixteen or less.

Puberty is associated with a spurt of growth more rapid than anything since early infancy. The average age for peak growth in girls in Europe and North America is 12, while for boys it is 14; boys, however, reach a peak *rate* of growth of 9 cm per year, compared with a typical peak rate for girls of 7.5 cm per year. So most boys end up taller than most girls. These physical and sexual developments are obvious and familiar to most of us. We do not have space here to go into much detail about the physical changes associated with puberty and adolescence. But most people are far less aware of the equally dramatic mental changes going on at this time, so perhaps they are worthy of mention.

The key cognitive development, as Piaget pointed out, is the ability, for the first time, to think in abstract terms. It is only in late adolescence that concepts like justice become meaningful to people, and it is only at this stage of development that they become capable of the kind of abstract reasoning involved in most scientific thought, for example. The turmoil caused by the individual's awareness of the dramatic bodily changes he or she is experiencing, and the resulting shift in the individual's self-image, tend to obscure, except to psychologists and the better kind of teacher, the much deeper changes in reasoning power – quality as well as quantity – that are happening at the same time. Adolescents begin to try out new roles, from different styles of hair and clothing to hero worship of sports or rock stars, or even espousing, usually briefly, extreme religious cults or political movements. This is all part of the testing out of their new bodies and new capacity for reasoning. Sometimes the results are naive, in adult terms; but the developing adult learns from experience – another crucial human characteristic.

Inevitably, sex roles become important. In early adolescence, boys and girls play in separate, single-sex groups. Later, groups of opposite sex begin to associate with one another, and these interactions lead to the formation of new, mixed-sex cliques. Finally, couples within these cliques begin to associate primarily with one another; the group disintegrates and the important relationship is one-to-one, boy-girl (or man-woman) interaction.

The result of all this is a sexually mature, physically adult naked ape, equipped with a very large brain, remarkable reasoning power, and an ability for complex verbal communication of ideas and information that far outstrips that of any other creature on Earth. Eighteen years of slow growth and development represents the longest childhood of any species we know; but the marathon of life is only just beginning for an 18 year old human being. What were the environmental pressures that made this long, slow process of development such a success, in evolutionary terms?

THE QUALITY OF HUMANITY

Neoteny, the slowing down of development, is the process which explains *how* our species got to be the naked ape with the big brain. But neoteny does not explain *why* this step in the evolution of our ancestors proved so successful. Obviously it had a great deal to do with the development of our brains. We can see from the fossil record how quickly, and how recently, brain growth took off in our ancestors. We still cannot be sure exactly what pressures placed intelligence at a premium, nor can we do more than guess as to whether our nakedness is a simple side effect of the neotonous development that made for large brains or whether it carried some selective advantage in itself. But there are two plausible, and thought provoking, hypotheses about this phase of human evolution that deserve at least a passing mention, even in a book that is primarily concerned with the nature of being human today and not with how we got to be the way we are.

The increase in the size of the brains of our ancestors in the direct line that led to man over the past four million years is impressive. About four million years ago, the varieties of proto-man whose fragmentary remains survive in parts of Africa had brains with a volume of some 400 cm^3, about a quarter of a pint, much the same as the size of the brain of a modern chimpanzee. The probable ancestors of ours from three million years ago were australopithecines: *Australopithecus afarensis*, with a brain size only slightly more than this, was probably the ancestor of both the *Homo* line and the two other australopithecines, *africanus* and the slightly bigger *robustus*, which had a brain capacity a little above 500 cm^3. The experts are still debating the exact relationship between these two australopithecines and ourselves (our own version of the story is given at the end of this book), but it is clear that, by about two million years ago, a third species and a still larger brain existed alongside them. Chiefly on the grounds of its brain size, not far off 700 cm^3, this species is the earliest to be given the name *Homo* – *Homo habilis*.

Within the space of the past two million years, through a clear line of evolutionary descent, brain size expanded to an average of some 900 cm^3 in early forms of *Homo erectus* (1.6 million years ago), 1100 cm^3 in late *Homo erectus* (just over 500 000 years ago), no less than 1500 cm^3 in our close relation *Homo sapiens neanderthalis*, which was around until a few tens of thousands of years ago, and 1400 cm^3, on average, in our own species, *Homo sapiens sapiens*. For a long time, students of evolution were to some extent over-impressed by this rapid increase in brain size, which they regarded as all-important in determining human nature. They failed to appreciate fully just how much of this increase in brain size was simply due to the increase in body size down this evolutionary line, following the simple rule that bigger bodies generally house bigger brains. *Australopithecus africanus*, for example, not only had a brain the size of a chimp's brain, but a body the size of a chimp's body! A typical *Homo habilis*, though, would stand just under five feet tall, and weigh in at under 45 kg, (100 pounds). It had a body only slightly bigger than that of a chimpanzee, but a brain almost twice as large as a chimp's. So there was some additional development of the brain, but if simply the *size* of the brain were indeed all-important, how was it that Neanderthal man, with his bigger brain, was supplanted by ourselves? The question is put into even sharper perspective by the huge variation in the size of 'normal' human brains from one individual to the next. Jonathan Swift's impressive 2000 cm^3 makes a puzzling counterpart to Anatole France's mere 1000 cm^3. Humans with very small brains, suffering from microcephaly, may have a brain only 600 cm^3 in size, scarcely 100 cm^3 greater than that of a gorilla, and yet, although of very limited intelligence, they will be very much human beings, with the ability, shared by no gorilla, to learn language in a human way.

Modern studies of the evolution of the brain use two related lines of attack. First, they relate brain size to body size, as far as this is possible. Secondly, thanks to pioneering work by Ralph Holloway, of Columbia University, in New York, they are able to analyse the *quality* of the brains that were housed in the fossil skulls they dig up.

Holloway's technique depends on making casts from the skulls, and fragments of skulls, that survive. In life, the skull fits closely over the brain, so using the skull as a mould he can make a cast which shows, faintly, the outlines of the brain that used to live within the skull. The outlines that are produced in this way are faint, but clearly discernible to the expert eye. And they have thrown up surprises, since the early 1970s, that we can best understand by looking first, briefly, at the way the human brain is organized.

Our brains are divided into two almost equal halves, the left brain and the right brain. Each half of the brain is made up of four distinct parts, called lobes, and these are identified with specific functions. The frontal lobe, for example, controls movement and is involved in emotions; at the back, the occipital lobe deals with vision; to the side is the temporal lobe, which is important for memory; and on top is the parietal lobe, which seems to play a major part in analysing the flow of information reaching the brain through the senses. For the present investigation, the key fact is that in the human brain the parietal and temporal lobes are relatively much larger and dominate the space available inside the skull, whereas in other apes these parts of the brain are much smaller. The key discovery that emerges from Holloway's work is that the small brains of ancestral hominids that lived three million years ago already show this characteristically human structure. In terms of the *kind* of brain housed within those small skulls, *Homo habilis* was certainly already human, and the australopithecines may well have been.[2]

Now comes the other part of the new insight. Heinz Stephan and colleagues at the Max Planck Institute for Brain Research, in Frankfurt, made a painstaking study of the size and weight of different parts of the brain from many living species, and compared these with body weights. From all these data they developed a 'progression index' which related brain size to body weight in closely related species. For an average modern man, the index value is 28.8 – but this conceals the usual wide variation in human brain size, which makes any value of the index from 19 to 53 'normal'. For a chimp, the equivalent figure is 12.0. The rules developed by Stephan's team have also been used to calculate the equivalent index values for our ancestors. According to these figures, and assuming a weight of 18 kg (40 pounds) for *Australopithecus afaransis*, our ancestor from three million years ago already had a progression index value of 21.4, as high as that of some individual human beings today. The figure for *Homo erectus* is 26.6. So Holloway concludes the 'the human brain appeared very much earlier than the time when *H. erectus* emerged,' and that '*Australopithecus* and at least one other African primate of the period from three million to one million years ago had brains that were essentially human in organiza- tion … so far as the subsequent absolute cranial enlargement is concerned, the major mechanism involved, although surely not the only one, appears to have been that as hominids grew larger in body their brains enlarged proportionately.'

So the primary characteristic that makes us human was already established three million years ago. This is very soon after the date set by the molecular biologists for the split between our line and the line leading to the chimpanzees, about 4.5 million years ago. And the convergence of the evidence clearly points to some key event, or events, that occurred around four to five million years ago and set our ancestors on the path that led to ourselves. The kind of development that occurred to produce the identifiably human features of the brain is linked with the complexities of human behaviour and social interac- tions. Evidence of tool making and the beginnings of 'human' society, in the form of camp sites, are found for the first time at around the same landmark period, some three million years ago. So in order to find the environmental pressures that made us human, we have to look for changes, happening around four or five million years ago, that favoured more complex social groupings, an ability for individuals to behave in cooperation with one another, and the ability to process complex information from their senses about the surrounding terrain rapidly and effectively. Once such complex social groups got started, of course, their increasing sophistication would itself feed back on the evolving brains to select those qualities which made for even more effective cooperation. In a similar way, a brain honed to be flexible and absorb new ideas would both produce a tool-making culture and be refined by the practices of a tool-making culture into an even more recognizably 'human' organ. We can even identify the major environmental changes that occurred four or five million years ago, that must have been instrumental in establishing the proto-human line. But the evidence is too sparse for the experts to agree on the details of that first stage of human evolution.

Marathon Man – or Aquatic Woman?

As several critics of the term 'naked ape' have pointed out, we are not, in fact, hairless. It is just that our hairs are very fine and rather short. But this is something of a red herring, since the absence of long, thick fur is still a striking human characteristic, and the image conjured up by the popular catch phrase is a good one. Whatever the processes were that made us human, they involved transforming a tree-climbing ape into an upright walker on the plains. Tree climbing is actually a very good preparation for walking – at least, the kind of tree climbing practised by our ancestors was. It involves swinging along underneath branches, hand over hand, and evolutionary adaptations for this kind of lifestyle involved changes in the arrangement of the body to make it more upright, a flexible shoulder joint, changes in the position of the head and neck on top of the body, and many others. These adaptations for brachiation, as it is called, and their usefulness in adapting to a life on two legs, are discussed in more detail in *The Monkey Puzzle*.

Life in the trees also sharpened the senses of our ancestors, and put information processing and intelligence, of a sort, high on the list of selective advantages. A tree-climbing ape has to be able to judge accurately which branches will bear its weight, and whether it is safe to jump (or swing) from one branch to another. Accurate three-dimensional vision is essential, and colour vision is also a great asset in helping to select food from the available leaves, fruit and berries. Once adapted to such a lifestyle, it seems unlikely that the successful tree-dwelling apes would ever leave it, but what seems to have happened is that the lifestyle left them.

Around five million years ago, in round terms, a major change in the environment of our planet took place. Because of changes in geography caused by continental drift, which blocked off the flow of warm water to polar regions and allowed the poles to freeze, the world entered into a long Ice Epoch, within which full Ice Ages ebbed and flowed, separated by shorter warm intervals called interglacials.[3] One effect of this, both because water was locked up as ice and because of associated changes in the circulation of the atmosphere, was that the region of East Africa where our ancestors lived dried out. The forest retreated, giving way to more open plains and savannah.

Even so, the most successful tree-apes would still have found a home in the dwindling forests. But their slightly less successful cousins would have been pushed out onto the fringes of the dwindling forests, to make a new home, or die, on the plains. Many must have died; we are descended from the few who first adapted and then evolved to suit the new conditions.

The changes that made our ancestors successful in this new environment included intelligence and adaptability, learning among other things to cooperate with one another and to scavange the remains of meat killed by hunters such as the large cats. David Carrier, of the University of Michigan, thinks that it was at this point that our relative nakedness also evolved and became important. Although human beings run more slowly than many other animals – our top speed compares with that of a startled chicken – we can keep up a steady jog for hour after hour. This is partly because we are able to keep cool by sweating profusely, and also because we are not covered by thick fur. Most mammals keep cool by panting, which is less efficient as a means of reducing body heat, and although they may be able to sprint very rapidly for a short time, the by-product of this activity is a sharp rise in body temperature, so they soon have to stop to cool off. Carrier suggests that naked skin and sweating evolved alongside running at a steady pace for hours, enabling proto-humans to chase down and kill game simply by outlasting it. The hypothesis has its attractions, not least since it offers an explanation for an unusual and distinctive human characteristic, the ability to run slowly for long distances – something which, if you think about it, is rather hard to understand any other way in terms of natural selection. But the marathon man idea is on shakier ground in some other respects, not least because the human body has only a small storage capacity for water, so that a marathon runner is in great danger from dehydration, especially on the dry African plains.

Which brings us rather neatly to what is surely the most seductive hypothesis for our nakedness, the idea that our ancestors spent a significant part of their evolutionary history as semi-aquatic animals, wading in shallow seas and lakes, and diving for food.

The idea came originally in 1960, from Sir Alister Hardy, and was published in the *New Scientist* (vol. 7, p. 642). It was taken up by Elaine Morgan in 1972 in a popular book *The Descent of Woman*, and presented in more complete form by the same author in 1982, in *The Aquatic Ape*. The argument includes evidence such as the proven ability of people to dive efficiently (compared with, say, cattle or lions), the smoothness and hairlessness of our streamlined bodies, the distribution of fat beneath our skin (reminiscent of the blubber of a dolphin, but unlike any other primate), and, shades of the marathon man idea, sweating. According to Morgan, however, sweating is a very bad way to control body heat, because it involves the loss of valuable salts through the skin, as well as water. She links sweating with our ability to cry salt tears as an adaptation to eliminate the salts that would otherwise, in a marine environment, build up to excess in the body. And, of course, the 'mystery' of our lack of water storage capability is less of a mystery if we evolved, for a time, within the water itself.

Many of the points raised by Hardy and Morgan merit serious attention, and the aquatic ape hypothesis is certainly taken more seriously today than it was when it first appeard. Scientific papers discussing the implications of the aquatic ape idea now crop up from time to time in respectable scientifc journals. Even while we were writing this book we came across two new examples: a paper called 'The aquatic ape theory: evidence and a possible scenario', by the Dutch scientist Mar Verhaegen, in *Medical Hypotheses*, vol. 16, p. 17, and a new investigation of the diving reflex of Massaud Mukhtar and John Patrick (*Journal of Physiology*, vol. 370, p. 13). The latter is especially interesting, since their tests show that simply immersing a person's face in a bowl of cold water enables an average subject to hold his or her breath for nearly 66 seconds, compared with 57 seconds when the face is in air. And in August 1987 Michael Crawford, of the Nuffield

Laboratory of Comparative Medicine, suggested to a meeting of the British Association for the Advancement of Science that the large human brain developed as a response to a diet rich in fish, which contain polyunsaturated fats that provide the chemical food needed to build big brains. Which ties in neatly with the aquatic ape hypothesis. We like the idea enormously, and, accepting that all such ideas about human origins are in a sense 'just so stories', this is probably the best. But it suffers from two serious difficulties. The first is with timing. The molecular evidence, the brain casts and the environmental changes all point to about 4.5 million years ago as the crucial time when the line leading to mankind became established. Yet by three million years ago our ancestors were firmly established on the African plains. Was there time for them to have entered upon an aquatic way of life (which certainly could be a satisfactory response to the shrinking of the forests and drying out of the land) and then to give it all up and go back to dry land? We simply do not know, but palaeontologists and anthropologists who do take the hypothesis seriously ought to be looking for ways around this difficulty. Morgan herself has not taken full account of the molecular evidence or the brain casts, and gives incorrect dates for the emergence of the human line. And the other problem is why our supposedly successful aquatic ancestors should ever have left the seas at all. There were no major global environmental shifts at the right time to force the aquatic ape out of the water, although there is evidence that the seaward end of the great African rift valley system flooded and then dried out between about 6.7 million years ago and five million years ago. The coincidence of this geological dating with the other dates in the story we have outlined is certainly striking, and we believe that more could be made of the connection. The australopithecines, on this picture, would have been the first naked apes, as well as the first one with human-type brains, forced out of the water and onto the East African plains as the region dried out. But Hardy himself originally suggested that 20 million years of a semi-aquatic existence would be needed to produce the evolutionary changes he and Morgan have described, and there is nothing like this timespan available in the light of modern evidence.

The story has probably been taken as far as it can be by amateurs, no matter how gifted – Morgan herself is a talented writer, the geological evidence comes (hardly surprisingly) from geologists, and Hardy, although a zoologist, never took up the challenge of preparing a complete version of the idea he tossed out on 5 March 1960 to the members of the British Sub-Aqua Club, meeting in Brighton on the south coast of England. One day someone will take it seriously enough to do a thorough professional job of sorting the evidence and producing a coherent, consistent theory. Until then, we leave you with the best 'just so' story of human origins; perhaps not marathon man but, with a nod to Elaine Morgan, a long-distance (female) swimmer!

A 'just so' story gets its name from the eponymous tales of Rudyard Kipling, who 'explained' just how various creatures came to be the way they are (the leopard covered in spots, for example) with appealing, but definitely tongue-in-cheek, tales. In the way evolutionary biologists use the term today, to poke gentle fun at ideas they disagree with, a 'just so' story is a version of evolution, applied to a particular characteristic of a particular species, that is superficially appealing but most probably is *not* so!

Whichever of the 'just so' stories you fancy, however, there is no doubt at all that one of the most crucial developments in making us human – perhaps *the* most crucial development – was the evolution of language. Communication is the foundation of all mammalian social systems, including those of other primates, but none of them has the structural complexity of human societies and human language. Communication is the cornerstone of society, and we have a very clear idea of how our unique communicative abilities have evolved.

3

WORDS AND MUSIC

Speech is a uniquely human characteristic. Its importance goes without saying, so to speak – expressions in common use which themselves indicate the special role of speech in human lives. If we needed any confirmation of our commonsense understanding of the importance of speech to people, we need only look at the pages of a widely used student primer on the development of knowledge in human infants, where we find[1] that well over two-thirds of the entire book is taken up by the chapters on language acquisition. Our development of linguistic abilities today depends intimately on the structure of our brains, and the way that structure has evolved in the past few million years, as man has become something more than an ordinary ape. It is very much a part, a large part, of the one per cent advantage we have over the other apes, and understanding the way the brain has developed linguistic skills sheds insights on many features of what makes us human.

Infants develop language in a way which clearly resembles Piaget's idea of sensorimotor development. They start out with noises that reflect their personal feelings – crying when hungry or wet, contented cooing noises when warm and dry and fed – and develop their abilities and relationships outward into the world around them. By the age of four or five months, the infant is stringing whole series of sounds together to make noises called babbling. These noises include the ones that will later become part of normal speech, but also a lot more noises, including many that are used in speech of different languages. An American infant, for example, will not only make the kind of noises heard in everyday adult American speech, but also the kind of rolling 'r' sound typical of the French language, and the clicking noises, made with the tongue, that are part of the speech pattern in some African languages. The infant runs through a whole host of babbling noises, but in different parts of the world only some of these available human sounds have been picked out and used in speech, simply through accidents of history (and pre-history).

Babies babble even when left to their own devices. But several experiments have shown that they babble even more when somebody responds to them. Just a human figure leaning over the cot encourages a baby's babbling; when the human smiles at them, tickles their tummy, and makes 'baby talk' back at them they smile in return and babble even more. At this very early stage, they learn the value of communication as a way to get attention. (Why mothers, in particular, should be predisposed to spend their valuable time cooing over a baby and tickling its tummy is another interesting question, which we shall deal with in part III of this book.) But babbling is not language; it is a kind of trial run of the vocal apparatus. We can say that language begins when the infant starts to utter single words, some time in the six months or so after its first birthday, and then to combine words in pairs to make simple, telegraphic sentences, which may look incomprehensible in print but which are usually crystal clear from the context in which they are uttered.

First Words

In their first year, when children begin to use single words, each word can stand for a whole sentence. 'Foot' or 'cup' may simply be utterances that acknowledge the existence of objects in the child's world. But 'eat', from context, may quite clearly be shorthand for 'I want to eat', while 'dada', again depending on context, may mean 'daddy has come home' or it may mean 'daddy is not here at present'. In the next stage of language acquisition, between about $1\frac{1}{2}$ and $2\frac{1}{2}$ years of age, this develops into the use of two-word sentences. But the way in which the two words are used together reveals that the child has an intuitive grasp of some quite complex grammatical concepts.

All children, whatever their cultural background, make the same kind of two-word utterances at this stage. Hilgard and Atkinson, for example, quote equivalents from English, German, Russian and Samoan infants, all of whom say (in their own languages) the same sort of things – 'there book', 'give candy', 'allgone milk', 'hit ball', 'my shoe', 'big boat', 'where ball', and so on. The interesting thing about these 'sentences' – apart from the fact, once again, that in context an utterance such as 'see doggie' is as intelligible as the equivalent, much longer, adult expression – is that there are two *kinds* of words being used. There is a small number of words, called pivot words, which describe what things are doing, or their relationships – 'allgone', 'big', 'my' and so on. And there is a much larger number of words, called open words, that are essentially labels, or names, of things. Without being taught any rules of grammar, all children, all over the world, start to construct sentences as if obeying the rule that a sentence is made up of a pivot word and an open word – 'allgone boat', 'my doggie', or, say, 'daddy home'.

For the next ten years or more, the child develops its language skills by learning new words and constructing longer and more complicated sentences using them. Once communication has been established, of course, parents and teachers can 'correct' the child's use of language, informing him or her of mistakes and providing the official rules of grammar that society says we ought to obey. But where do those rules come from in the first place, and how does the child learn to communicate at all before acquiring enough language to understand the instructions passed on by adults? This is all the more interesting since children, of course, have their own instinctive ideas about grammar, ideas which are often more logical than the arbitrary rules imposed by society. A child will say 'I readed the book', or 'I hided the ball' almost automatically, and may have great trouble learning the irregularity of, in this example, verb endings. According to one of the leading modern theories of language acquisition, it is all because we are pre-wired, or ready programmed, to speak language from the moment we are born – indeed, from the moment of conception, since the coding must be carried, ultimately, in our DNA.

This is, incidentally, another example of how small the differences which make us human, rather than other animals, really are. We are programmed to learn grammatical languages, but grammar is only an extension of the kind of natural logic which all higher vertebrates (birds and mammals) share. A rat that learns to run a maze in order to get an edible reward, or a bird that learns to strip the top from a milk bottle to get at the cream, is also demonstrating, to a degree, a capacity for the same kind of learning. Even human language is not a unique, God-given facility, but rather a straightforward development, building on skills shared by many species, not just our ancestors.

WIRED FOR SOUND

The capacity for children to learn language instinctively is demonstrated very clearly by the private language that develops between twins, or other close siblings. We know personally, for example, a family in which twin girls have an elder sister, born just eleven months before they were. According to their parents and other members of the family, all three girls used to have a private language of their own, a means of communication which they all used until the eldest was about four. For a while, the older child, linguistically more developed than the younger two, was able to interpret some of their utterances for her parents. And the effectiveness of this language was demonstrated when the twins were barely two, at a garden picnic where several adults were present who all later agreed on the sequence of events.

Unknown to the adults, the two smaller girls were playing, out of sight behind some bushes, near the bank of a stream. Their older sister was with the adults at the picnic when one of the twins emerged from the bushes, chattering away, as far as the adults were concerned, incomprehensibly. The older sister immediately turned to her mother, tugging at her skirt and saying, in an agitated manner, 'Ruth in the water'. This precipitated a rush of adults to the stream, where, indeed, the other twin was to be seen floating away (admittedly fairly happily, buoyed up by air in her clothes) and was promptly rescued.

This is a specific example, reported to us by reliable witnesses who were present at the time. More generally, many scientific studies report how children left to their own devices develop their own 'pidgin' language, and one of the most widely quoted examples from recent decades is the effect of a sudden influx of immigrants into Hawaii earlier this century. The adult immigrants spoke many different languages – Japanese, American English, Malay and others. But within a generation a new language, Hawaiian Creole, appeared as children from these different backgrounds grew up together and incorporated elements from all the languages they were exposed to into their automatic system of language acquisition.

There are different theories put forward by scientist to explain the details of how this process works. But one of the leading contenders, which fits in very neatly with all that we know about human origins and evolution, is the proposal first put forward by the American linguist Noam Chomsky in the mid-1960s. Chomsky started from the fact that the ability to learn language and use it is part of our genetic inheritance. He said that every child must therefore be born with a very specific predisposition to understand the grammatical structures of language, in the sense of the pivot and open word structures that are so common in infant speech, and also at a deeper level. The infant possesses, in Chomsky's terminology, a 'language acquisition device', or LAD. Nobody has located the LAD physically in the human body. If it does exist, it is probably the diffuse product of interactions involving different parts of the nervous system, as well as the ears and vocal parts of the mouth. But it is convenient to think of the LAD as a physical entity, a part of the nervous system which is wired up, by the development processes laid down in the DNA of our genes, to recognize instinctively the existence of words and of subgroupings of words such as nouns and verbs.

This idea explains why children do not need formal instruction in the rules of grammar in order to learn to speak. What they learn is the specific kind of speech they are exposed to – a Texan accent, for example, and a specific language, American English. But the way the words are put together within that language, or dialect, follows rules that are build into the child, and are the same for all human children and all human languages. Chomsky's theory, although controversial when it was first mooted is now widely accepted and, with modifications, forms the basis of a great deal of psychological research into language acquisition. But we are more concerned here with the evolution of language, as part of the one per cent advantage we have over the other apes. In that context, although the psychological insights are interesting, they are not so interesting, or important, as the biological features of the human body which provide us with the ability to speak and to understand language. And when we look at those features of the body, and especially at the structure of the human brain, we find very close links with the way human intelligence has evolved, as well as curious hints of new insights, as yet far from fully developed, into how individual people operate as members of a complex society.

Broca's Brains

Our linguistic abilities are clearly a feature of the way our brains are put together, not simply of their size. In extreme cases, dwarfs with very small brains, or people who are normal in body size but have small brains, still acquire language. Nor, indeed, is high intelligence required in order to learn language; children with very limited intelligence begin to acquire language in exactly the same way as other children, following the normal route to language acquisition. The difference is simply that they do not proceed so far down the usual path as children with normal intelligence. One of the overall features of the human brain is the way in which the surface (the cortex) is folded and convoluted, so that it provides a much larger area than that of the cortex of a smooth brain; this is a feature thought to be of great importance to human intelligence. But there are also structures within the brain, and it is the presence of these structures, even in a reduced form, that seems to contribute to our linguistic abilities.

Superficially, a normal human brain seems to be composed of two mirror-image hemispheres, linked to each other by bundles of nerve fibres. The most important of these links between the left and right sides of the brain is called the corpus callosum. The two sides of the brain are in communication with one another through these nerve fibres, but there is an important division of labour between them. Roughly speaking, each half of the brain controls half of the body, but in most people the *right* half of the brain controls the *left* arm, leg and so on, while the *left* half of the brain controls the *right* hand and arm, leg, and so on. And, thanks to many studies of people who have suffered various forms of brain damage, we now know that important parts of the brain responsible for speech – speech centres – are located in the left brain.

The breakthrough came from work by a young surgeon, Paul Broca, in Paris in the 1860s. In fact, other people had suspected a division of labour between the hemispheres of the brain which gave special responsibility for speech to the left hemisphere, but it was Broca who convinced the medical world, and in his honour one of the key speech centres is now known as Broca's area. Strokes or other physical damage which affected the left side of the brain were, he found, almost always associated with speech difficulties among his patients; but similar damage to the right side of the brain left their linguistic abilities intact.

This work, and the work of Broca's successors down the years, has shown that the problems are not simply caused by a physical difficulty in producing the sounds required for speech. Patients with damaged Broca's areas are incapable of expressing certain ideas, and produce a telegraphic kind of speech in which, for example, if asked to describe a recent trip the patient may simply respond with the world 'London' and when pressed to produce a sentence describing the trip will say 'Go London'. Damage to another part of the left hemisphere, Wernicke's area (named after another nineteenth-century pioneer), produces a different kind of language difficulty. The speech of such a patient sounds normal at first hearing, but the patient has lost some words entirely, and puts in substitutions or circumlocutions. Instead of using the word 'hammer', for example, such a patient may use 'spade'; or the patient may use a circumlocution, 'a thing you hit things with', or simply drop in a filler word such as 'thing'.

More insights into the different roles played by the two hemispheres of the brain have come from research on patients who have undergone what is graphically called 'split-brain' surgery. The original reasoning behind this operation, first carried out in the 1940s, was that it might help patients suffering from some forms of epilepsy. The operation is now largely discredited, but the victims of it have still provided information about how brains work. Details are not for the squeamish, but in such patients the bundle of nerves joining the two hemispheres of the brain, the corpus callosum and/or other nerve fibres, has been severed, so there is no way for information in one hemisphere to pass to the other side of the brain. The left brain still controls the right arm and hand, for example, but quite literally the right brain does not know what the left brain is doing - except, in this example, if the person looks with half the field of view of each eye (the left half) to see what the right hand is up to. Astonishingly, in many cases such people are able to lead essentially normal lives, but by severing the connection between the two halves of the brain, surgery has created people with a remarkable division of linguistic abilities.

This is tested by providing information to only one half of the brain at a time. In experiments which are set up so that visual images are presented only to one field of view at a time, for example, the importance of the left brain for speech becomes very clear. Information from the left field is directed by nerve fibres to the right brain, and vice versa. So when a split-brain patient is shown a picture of, say, a cup, flashed to the right field only, the patient has no difficulty reporting in speech what he or she has seen. The same patient, however, shown the same image flashed on a divided screen in such a way that only the left field (and therefore the right brain) can see it will report that nothing was visible. Nothing *was* visible to the left brain, which is the one doing the talking. But when asked to reach under a screen with the left hand (controlled, remember, by the right brain) and pick out by feel the object that has just been pictured, invariably the patient gets it right, sight unseen. Information can still get in to the right brain and be used, but it cannot reach across to the left brain to report what it has seen in speech. This is not just an inability of the right brain to get its hand on the levers that control the vocal cords and mouth; it will not respond to printed instructions flashed onto the screen (although the left brain will respond, for example, to the printed word 'smile' flashed to the right field of view). Words are, predominantly, in the province of the left hemisphere.

Whole books have been written about the special roles of the left brain and the right brain in human beings, and the fascinating minor exceptions which help to 'prove the rule'.[2] It is such an important topic that we shall soon return to it again ourselves, if only briefly. But in terms of understanding human evolution the first important thing we have learned is that speech is associated with the left hemisphere of the brain, the same hemisphere that controls the right hand. It may be more than a coincidence that the 'handedness' which dominates among people is associated with the side of the brain in which linguistic centres have developed. And, whether or not this speculation stands up, simply knowing that certain features of the left brain are linked with language gives a new benchmark for deciding how human our ancestors were.

EVOLUTIONARY IMPLICATIONS

Ralph Holloway's technique of taking brain casts from fossil skulls provides some tantalizing hints at the date when human linguistic abilities began to be significant. Studies of people with damaged brains show that the sentences we speak seem to be organized according to the underlying grammatical rules by Wernicke's area (so, perhaps, at least part of the LAD *can* be physically located!) and are then turned into speech by the way the Broca's area controls movement of lips, tongue, and the rest of the talking apparatus. Both these areas are on the left side of the brain, and are developed more, in humans, than the corresponding regions of the right hemisphere of the brain. The left hemisphere of the brain of a normal person today is larger than the right, and bulges into a corresponding dent inside the skull. A skull cast from a modern skeleton would quite clearly show the difference between the two hemispheres.

When it comes to the fossil skulls the difficulties of detecting such subtleties are enormous. It is something of a miracle that Holloway is able to get good casts at all, working with damaged pieces of fossil skull; in very many cases, even when the skull is more or less complete, it has been distorted so that no direct comparison of the two hemispheres is possible. And, of course, we must assume that the swelling over the speech centres was smaller millions of years ago, when our ancestors were just beginning to talk. And yet, in spite of all these difficulties, there is just a hint of the sought-for swelling in a skull of *Homo habilis*, a type which lived just over two million years ago. *Habilis* represents the oldest human ancestor that was not also an ancestor of the chimpanzees and gorillas. The trace of the Broca's area is rather more marked in skulls from *Homo erectus*, the species that followed *habilis* and represents our own immediate ancestor. It was *erectus* that spread *Homo* out from the cradle of East Africa and around the world, across into Asia and north into Europe. Tantalizingly, another branch of the ancestral ape family, the australopithecines, also show an enlargement

65

of this part of the brain a couple of million years ago, suggesting that they too might have begun to develop speech. But since their lines went extinct, they literally represent a dead end in the study of evolution – unless you accept the speculation aired by one of us in *The Monkey Puzzle*, and elaborated on in the Appendix to the present book, that the australopithecines may have been the ancestors of the chimp and gorilla.

A lot of this evidence is speculative – circumstantial evidence at best. But the date of the earliest hint of a developing Broca's area in the brains of our ancestors, a little over two million years ago, ties in intriguingly with the earliest dates of known tool use by *Homo*, about two and a half million years ago. The early tools are crude until about one and a half million years ago, and then archaeologists find much more sophisticated stone hand axes, the beginning of a genuine tool-making technology which developed further as time went on. Holloway in particular links the increasing sophistication of tool making with the development of language. He argues that both processes involve the same kind of thought – planning out a sequence of steps that must be carried through in order to produce, in one case, a complete tool, and in the other a complete sentence. In both cases, if some steps are left out or carried out wrongly, the result is useless.

Other archaeologists and anthropologists have suggested that the ability to carry out finely controlled movements of the hands, essential in tool making, could have led to the development of sign language, and Gordon Hewes, of the University of Colorado, is one of those who have pointed out the way in which many people unconsciously move their tongues while carrying out delicate manual tasks – and the author typing these words into his computer immediately became aware, as he did so, that he was doing precisely that, sticking his tongue out of the side of his mouth to 'help him concentrate' on the typing!

Most people are right handed. Their dominant hand is controlled by the left hemisphere of the brain, where areas responsible for both the grammatical construction of language and the physical manipulation of the mouth parts by which we speak are located. A right-handed typist (or stone axe maker) may naturally find the dominant part of his or her brain playing games with the mouth parts while the right hand is at work. Could there be more to all this, though? Could it be that the very reason that the left brain became the centre for language was that is had already evolved special abilities linked with tool making (and perhaps sign language) in a predominately right-handed population? The area of the brain that controls fine movements of the right hand indeed lies very close to the area that controls fine movements of the all-important tongue and other speech organs.

Once again, new evidence along these lines came in while this book was in preparation. Nicholas Toth, of the University of California, Berkeley, has been studying shaped stones from sites at Koobi Fora on the east side of Lake Turkana in northern Kenya. The pattern of flaking shows that these stone tools from about two million years ago were made by striking a hammerstone held in the right hand onto a stone being held in the left hand.[3] Such evidence, together with that of the early development of the Broca's region of the brain, strengthens the case that there was no long gap between the evolution of tool-making skills and speech, and that the two went literally hand in hand with the appearance of *Homo habilis* on the scene.

None of these speculations *prove* anything about the origins of language, but they offer fascinating hints. In this picture, it might just be an accident that one hemisphere developed in this way, so that most people today are right handed and have linguistic skills. However, that leads us up against another puzzle, one which brings us up to date in evolutionary time and also in terms of the way evolutionary theorists think about species, including the human species, today. Why, if being a right-handed linguist is such a good thing, are there any left-handed people in the world? And why, in particular, has the proportion of left-handed people in the population stayed the same ever since our ancestors were chipping away at stone tools in East Africa, a couple of million years ago?

THE RIGHT-HANDED APE

About 90 per cent of human beings are right-handed. This is unusual in the animal kingdom, although not quite unique. Some species of parrot tend to favour the use of one claw for feeding and the other to stand on, while according to legend most polar bears are left-handed (or left-pawed) (but there has been an understandable reluctance amongst zoologists to test this particular legend by offering to shake hands with a polar bear). In most of the animal kingdom, either individual creatures are what we would term ambidextrous, or, where individuals favour the use of one paw (as in many rats), the choice of favoured paw is arbitrary, with half the population of that species favouring the left and half favouring the right. The bias in people is due to dominance of the left hemisphere of the brain, which controls the right side of the body. Some studies suggest that the bias extends out into the world beyond our bodies – most people, for example, when asked to judge the length of a rod by touch, tend to be more accurate when the rod is on the left side of their body, regardless of which hand they touch the rod with. And this bias is nothing new.

About ten per cent of people seem to have been left-handed throughout recorded history, judging by the handwriting of the records themselves and evidence such as the direction of brush strokes on paintings. Pushing back still further into the past, our ancestors who went in for cave paintings often left the imprint of one hand on the cave wall – perhaps as a kind of signature, or perhaps for some reason now lost to us. There, the image is almost always that of the left hand, exactly what you would expect if the outline was being traced by a right-handed painter. And experts who have tried to reproduce the kind of stone tools that our ancestors used more than two million years ago, using the same technique of chipping away at one stone with another, have found that the old tools were shaped by being held in the left hand and chipped at with the right, and that the end product, a stone axe or whatever, is shaped to nestle comfortably in the right hand.

This may, just possibly, indicate the origins of our right-handedness. Perhaps, just by chance, the first tool maker(s) happened to be right-handed. As they taught others the tricks of their trade, they would naturally teach them to hold tools in the same way. Left-handers who tried the new skill would find it difficult; using their 'unnatural' hand, they would make bad tools, be unsuccessful hunters and fail to achieve enough in stone age society to obtain a mate and leave children behind to carry their left-handed genes. It is a highly dubious 'just so' story, which has the sole merit of linking the rise of right-handedness with the emergence of *Homo habilis* the tool user; the advantage of this is that since even our closest relatives the chimps show 50:50 split between those which favour their right hand and those which favour their left it is likely that the genetic bias arose more recently than the man-ape split, which happened some four or five million years ago. *Homo habilis* is the first ancestor on our side of the split.

And the bias *is* genetic, although the genetic basis is far from simple. Left-handedness runs in families, but in a complicated way suggesting that at least two separate genes, and perhaps more, are involved. We need not, fortunately, go into the details, but a nice example of the genetic predisposition for handedness comes from Scotland, where the Kerr clan was so well known for its left-handers that they gave the term 'corrie fisted', meaning left-handed, to the language. At Kerr Castle, in Jedburgh, all the spiral staircases have left-handed twists, which made them easy to defend by left-handed swordsmen backing up the stairs. Unfortunately, that also means that the twists were convenient for right-handed swordsmen attacking *up* the stairs, but you cannot have everything.

'Corrie-fisted' is, of course, a term sometimes used in derogatory fashion. Other languages have also given us synonyms for left-handedness with unpleasant connotations. 'Sinister' and 'gauche' are two obvious examples. And in the Bible, where do the favoured ones get to sit? Where else but at God's *right* hand. Even the word 'right' itself denotes both a direction and the correct, proper or good way to do things. For as long as right-handers have dominated society, it seems, left-handers have been regarded as unpleasant weirdos. Perhaps this is simply the instinctive dislike of the majority of anyone out of the usual rut, but perhaps there is more to it.

Cack-handers have been accused, down the ages, of everything from deviousness to mental deficiency and witchcraft, and the mere fact of their left-handedness can still arouse hostility in any right-hander attempting to teach them manual tasks. It is much easier to teach a group of children – or adults – a skill such as writing or knitting if they all use the same dominant hand, and as most people are right-handed the pressure has often been on the left-handed to conform rather than to obey their natural instincts. A generation ago, the British psychologist Sir Cyril Burt noted that, whereas (by his estimate) five per cent of the ordinary school population in Britain was left-handed, the proportion of cack-handers in special schools for 'mental defectives' was 12 per cent. To Burt, the obvious implication was that left-handedness was linked with mental backwardness; today we can see that many of the more intelligent children had learned to cover up their left-handedness and conform, while the less able children in the special schools, who had enough trouble coping with the rest of life, were simply doing what came naturally. The proportion of 10 or 12 per cent left-handers in those schools is, indeed, typical of all human populations around the world, although there are some minor differences from place to place and the proportion of left-handed men is greater than the proportion of left-handed women.

Today the educational system, in Britain and many other countries, operates on a more enlightened basis. It is official policy that children should use whichever hand they prefer for writing and other tasks involving manual dexterity (another word containing right-handed bias!), whether their more dextrous hand is 'right' or not. So there are more left-handers around today who have, as it were, come out of the closet compared with a few decades ago, even though the world is still largely set up for the benefit of right-handers.

Whether or not a person is left-handed is generally judged by which hand they used for writing, although there are many people who do some things right-handed and others left-handed. In cricket, for example, England bowler Graham Dilley bowls with his right arm but bats left-handed, while his colleague Derek Underwood did every-thing the other way around, bowling left arm and batting right-handed. A lot more research still needs to be done to find out just what differences in the brain, and genes, make one person left-handed and another right-handed. But along with our other unique features, including nakedness, intelligence, and speech, mankind is unique among the animals on Earth (leaving aside those parrots and the Polar bear legend) in having a preferred handedness. But still that population of left-handers has persisted, at the ten per cent level, from the stone age to modern times. We do not know what the reason is, but it does seem that this must be an example of what British evolutionary biologist John Maynard Smith has called an 'evolutionarily stable strategy' or ESS. And that tells us something else about the way evolution works.

THE STRATEGY OF LEFT AND RIGHT

Evolution proceeds because there is variety among the individuals of a species, and because there is selection of the individuals best fitted to their environment. The ones that are well adapted to their environment do best and leave more offspring then the less well fitted, so their genes spread. The competition in Darwinian evolution is not so much between different species, but between individual members of the same species. And Maynard Smith has given us a mathematical basis for understanding the individual strategies for survival.

This is all based on a branch of mathematics called games theory, which has been developed in sound mathematical detail in recent decades, originally because of its importance in 'modelling' different aspects of war and calculating the odds of success for different strategies in different situations. It carries across almost unchanged into the competition between individual members of a species to make best use of the resources available in the ecological niche occupied by that species.

The best way to give an idea of what games theory and ESS are all about is by an example, from Maynard Smith's work. This is the scenario of 'Hawks vs doves'.

Imagine, says Maynard Smith, a population of animals all of the same species. Each individual member of the population may behave either as a 'hawk', denoting aggressive behaviour, or as a 'dove', denoting peaceful behaviour. (In fact, doves are pretty aggressive birds, but they have come to symbolize peace in a metaphorical sense.) When a hawk finds a piece of food and another member of the species is present, it will always fight, if necessary, in an attempt to get the food. When a dove finds a piece of food but another member of the species is present, it will run away at once if attacked. If it meets another dove, it will try to bluff by making a threatening display, but will eventually leave the food and retreat. These are basic rules programmed into Maynard Smith's mathematical model. The question he then asked is, 'what proportion of hawks and doves represent a stable state of the population?'

This is a purely hypothetical example, so let us put some purely hypothetical (but sensible) numbers in, to indicate the value of the food the animals need. If the individual gets to eat the food, it scores 50 points. If it runs away, of course, it scores 0 points. If it gets in a fight and loses, it will be injured, and scores −100, and if it gets involved in a mutual threat display before running away, it scores −10 for the waste of time. The numbers are arbitrary, but they demonstrate the relative status of each possible outcome. We have taken these particular numbers from Richard Dawkins' book *The Selfish Gene*. The most successful individuals are the ones that eat most food and avoid getting hurt. So their genes wil be passed on to the next generation. The points are equated with reproductive success, and ESS theory addresses the question, 'is there a stable mixture of hawks and doves in the population which will persist from one generation to the next?'

The first thing that comes out of the calculation is that neither a population of all doves nor a population of all hawks is stable, in this sense. Consider doves first. If everyone is a dove, then every time there is a conflict both of the individuals produce a threat display which costs −10 points. But one of them runs away runs first, so the other one gets the food and scores 50 points, giving it a net gain of 40. The average 'score' is 15, by taking 40 and −10, adding them together and dividing by 2. So far so good. Everyone gets to eat, nobody gets hurt, and the all-dove society looks healthy. You can also see, from this very simple example, why many species of animal have evolved very elaborate and long-lasting threat displays, attempts to stare the opposition down without actually getting into a fight. People, like other animals, often do the equivalent.

But now consider what happens if one mutant hawk arises in the population. He does not waste time with threats; he just chases away the opposition and wins the prize every time, scoring 50 points. As long as hawks are rare, so that they do not very often meet one another and fight, they will do very well indeed, scoring 50 points where the doves are only scoring 15 on average, and so spread their genes throughout the population.

So what happens at the other end of the scale? In an all-hawk society, every meeting produces a bitter conflict. The winner scores 50 points, the loser scores −100, and the average is a pathetic −25. (Such a population would survive, of course, only so long as conflicts were rare and most food could be picked up without meeting another hawk and getting in a fight.) But what happens if a mutant dove appears? By running away every time a hawk threatens, and scoring 0 points in every conflict, but picking up food when nobody else is around, the dove does relatively well. So dove genes spread – up to a point.

Clearly, there must be a stable state somewhere between these extremes where the proportion of hawks and doves stays the same, and both strategies provide the same average gain in any conflict. For the particular numbers we have chosen here, the stable population contains five-twelfths doves and seven-twelfths hawks – fives doves for every seven hawks – and each individual scores 6.25 in each conflict, on average. In terms of real populations of real animals, we can recast this slightly. It is also a stable strategy for *each individual* to act like a hawk seven-twelfths of the time and to act like a dove five-twelfths of the time. Genes which operate on the body as if they were saying 'be aggressive just over half the time, but be a pacifist a bit less than half the time, and select at random which you are going to be in any one conflict' will be the most successful genes. The ESS can be either for each individual to play dove X per cent of the time, or for X per cent of the individuals to play dove all the time.

There is something peculiar, however, and significant about the numbers we have come up with. The ESS provides each individual with 6.25 points per conflict. The all-dove scenario gave each individual 15 points, more than twice as much. Every individual in the population would be better off if they were all doves – for 'the good of the species', the all-dove scenario is better than the ESS! But evolution does not work like that. It operates on individuals, not species, and the stable society is one in which, it turns out, every individual does worse than he or she could. This clearly has implications for human behaviour, and we shall come on to those in part III. But now, what can the ESS approach tell us about left-handedness?

It cannot tell us a lot, actually. The idea of research into the evolution of handedness is a new one which has not yet been taken up and given the attention we think it merits. But the evidence is that, throughout the time *Homo sapiens* has been on Earth, there has been a stable mix of 10 per cent left-handers and 90 per cent right-handers. Admittedly, the evidence is slight, but taking it at face value this *cannot* be a coincidence. If right-handers were at an absolute advantage, then genes for left-handedness would have died away, and while left-handers might still be around, their numbers would show a decline over the millenia. The balance is so clearly an example of an ESS that it must be that there are advantages in being a member of a minority group of left-handers in a population dominated by right-handers. Of course, maybe a population of all right-handers (or all left-handers) would be 'better' for the species. ESS theory says nothing about that. But the stable human population (leaving other factors aside) is one in which there are 10 left-handed people for every 90 right-handed people.

There have been suggestions recently that left-handedness maybe linked with the production of an unusually large amount of the hormone testosterone while the unborn child is developing in the womb. This seems to slow the growth of the left side of the brain, giving the right a chance to develop more and dominate. The idea is attractive, not least since it explains naturally why male babies, which produce more testosterone anyway, should turn out to be left-handed more often than female babies. You might think, at first sight, that this also pulls the rug from under the ESS idea, since it implies that the proportion of left-handers is an accident linked to minor changes in hormone levels. Not a bit of it. The question simply becomes 'why do hormone levels in unborn babies sometimes rise a little higher than usual – where "sometimes" means a precise proportion which has been the same for millions of years?' If being left-handed was bad for an individual, then genes which cause a high testosterone level would die out. The question simply moves back one step to become an ESS expressed in terms of testosterone instead of handedness!

In the early 1970s there was also an hypothesis around which claimed to link left-handedness with birth difficulties. The idea was that shortage of oxygen at birth might cause brain damage which in turn led to left-handedness. But that hypothesis, with its disturbing echoes of Burt's views on 'mental deficiency', was squashed in the early 1980s by a study based on the handedness of *all* the childen born in England, Wales and Scotland between 3 and 9 March 1958. Ian McManus, of Bedford College, in London, found from these data (which had lain around for years in the archives) that there is no correlation in this sample of more than 11 000 children between 'birth stress' and their inclinations at the age of seven to be right-handed, left-handed, or ambidextrous.

No, there is no getting away from it. Left-handers must carry some advantage in their genes, expressed in their behaviour and abilities, which makes the standard human mix of handedness an ESS. This does not necessarily mean that left-handers are 'good for the species', thought they might well be. It means that there is some advantage in being an individual member of a minority group of left-handers in a population dominated by right-handed people. We would expect those special features that enable left-handedness to survive in the human gene pool to be among the things people do well and other animals do badly, or not at all, since the balance between left and right in people is so unusual. And while there is no certain 'answer' to the puzzle yet, we can pinpoint several likely candidates.

WHEN LEFT IS RIGHT

Studies of split-brain patients, and other researches, have shown that there is a clear difference in the way the two halves of the brain work. We would like to say that the two halves of the brain 'think' differently, but we have to be careful about our choice of terms since some psychologists argue that the right brain does not think at all, in the uniquely human way that distinguishes us from the other animals. As well as being involved with language and delicate tasks such as typing or making stone axes, the left brain is responsible, in simplistic terms, for most of the logical and orderly processes that go to make us human. It is, in a sense, the 'scientific' side of the brain, where we are using the term 'scientific' in the stereotypical sense implying cold logic and reasoning – which is not, as it happens, the way most good scientists get their best ideas.

The right brain, however, is more emotional and, in the same kind of stereotyped terminology, 'artistic'. The left brain is more 'cerebral', if you like, but the right brain has its own specialized abilities too. From the enormous body of work which has been done in this area, we can pick out one or two examples which help to make the point, and we shall choose them from the world of music.

One of the earliest recorded cases dates back to 1745, when a man was the victim of a disease which left him paralysed over the entire right side of his body and unable to speak. Today, we infer that the illness had seriously affected his left brain. Yet, he was still able to sing, clearly and distinctly, hymns that he had learned before being taken ill, although he was incapable of learning new hymns. More recently, the Soviet composer Shebalin suffered a stroke which also affected his left brain, and after this he had great difficulty in speaking or in communicating by written words. But his ability to compose music was unimpaired. And there are several examples of the opposite effect – musicians who have suffered damage to the right brain and lost the ability to creat new compositions (or even to appreciate what were once favourite pieces of music) while still being able to use language as effectively as before.

In left-handed people, where, for whatever reason, the right brain dominates, we would expect the characteristically right-brain features to come to the fore, and left-brain abilities to take a back seat. Indeed, researchers have found that problems with reading such as dyslexia, or word blindness, are more common among left-handers than right-handers, as is stammering. But left-handed people are more likely to be artistic, musical, mathematical and good at judging distances and speeds. Perhaps this explains why there is a higher proportion of left-handers among top sports men and women, especially in games such as tennis, than in the population as a whole.

There are proportionately more left-handed architects than in the general population, and a study at Johns Hopkins University showed that children with very high levels of mathematical ability tend to be left-handed. Camilla Benbow and Julian Stanley examined the records of 100 000 children aged between 12 and 13 and found that more than 20 per cent of the 292 youngsters who scored at least 700 out of 800 in the mathematical section of the standard Scholastic Aptitude Test were left-handed – twice the average incidence of left-handedness in the population at large, and the data also confirm that boys are superior to girls in mathematical skills, with 13 times as many boys as girls scoring 700 or more in the maths tests. (Of course, there may be social effects at work here, since by the age of 12 girls may have 'learned' that they are not expected to do well at maths.) Because left-handedness is also more common in men and has now been linked with high levels of testosterone, Harvard researcher Norman Geschwind has argued that this explains why most great mathematicians and painters have been men, and why women have provided the best linguists. Whatever it is that makes for left-handedness may be at work in a more subtle way, enhancing right-brain activity, even among many men who are not obviously left-handed.

There is other, circumstantial, evidence that left-handers are simply superior to right-handers, in a more general sense, at least as long as they are members of a population dominated by right-handers. Leonardo da Vinci was a left-hander, and he represents the pinnacle of creative human achievement. He was both a great artist and a great scientist. Benjamin Franklin and Michelangelo, although slightly more specialized in their pursuits, were also great left-handers. Of course, we can all name left-handed people we know (and possibly love) who are not in the same league as these three gentlemen. But could their abilities tie in with another recent discovery by medical researchers?

In 1985, Sandra Witelson, of McMaster University in Ontario, reported finding that the corpus callosum is bigger in ambidextrous and left-handed people. The discovery is new, and is based on a limited number of studies of human brains. It has yet to be confirmed by other researchers. But it does suggest that in at least some left-handers the dominant role of the right brain is linked with a more efficient means of communication between the two halves of the brain. Perhaps this makes their brains more efficient, with two halves working together as one whole. Or, of course, it might just be that the dominant right brain has to channel some of its output through the conventional left-brain paths and that the growth of the corpus callosum represents an attempt to compensate for what is, in fact, a handicap. The idea that Leonardo had a brain in which the two halves were in more effective communication than in most of us is certainly attractive, however, even if it is a 'just so' story!

The difference between left and right brains has led to a whole mass of research that we cannot go into here. Princeton psychologist Julian Jaynes, for example, has argued that the emergence of consciousness and linguistic abilities in early man, or rather in the left brain of early man, is responsible for legends of people hearing 'voices in their heads', the voices of the gods, telling them what to do. God, say Jaynes, is just the left brain, struggling to break through into dominance and create a unified consciousness. And the noted writer Arthur Koestler was one of many people to point out the way in which creativity, including scientific creativity, is often linked with the idea of putting a problem to one side for a while, sleeping on it and waiting for the answer to emerge. Does the logical left brain shunt the problem over to the creative right brain, where it is solved and the answer handed back, ready to be dressed up in logical clothes?

Some researchers today argue that the right brain is still no more than an animal brain, driven by emotions and instincts alone, while all of human thinking comes from the left brain. But others – the majority – believe that it is the combination of left and right brain that makes us human. The old pattern of the brain in other species, with its bilateral structure, may simply have been a result of evolution for redundancy, a doubling up of an essential organ so that damage to one part of it need not be fatal. If one side of the brain was injured then, up to a point, the other could take over. But this provided an opportunity for our ancestors to take a new evolutionary step. Because of the existance of, in a sense, a 'spare' brain inside their skulls, there was scope for specialization to happen when one hemisphere, perhaps determined by chance, became responsible for fine manipulations and for language. At the same time, the other half of the brain had scope to develop special abilities for understanding relationships of things in space (and perhaps time), as well as art and music. By losing the safety net of the redundancy of having two identical brains, we have gained, in this picture, a new whole that is greater than the sum of its parts, and goes beyond mere duplication to provide two new kinds of skill.

How could this fit in with the balance of 10 per cent left-handers and 90 per cent right-handers in human society? Nobody really knows, but, not to be outdone by the likes of Geschwind, we can offer our own kite-flying speculation. If we look at the differences ascribed to the left and right brains, we would not be surprised to discover that right-handers (dominated by the left brain) are more logical and organized than left-handers (dominated by the right brain). It takes a lot of organization (and effective verbal and written communication) to set up and maintain a complex human society. This has obvious evolutionary advantages, and so a society created and dominated by right-handers would do well. But once such a society exists, surely there is room in it for a few dreamers, creative people who may not be very good at bureaucracy but are capable of throwing up bright new ideas from time to time, which the bureaucrats latch on to and make use of? The occasional Leonardo is well worth the 'cost' of a few layabout artists who make no contribution to food production or to running society efficiently. Or, recasting the scenario in individual terms (the proper Darwinian way to look at things), the success of an occasional left-handed genius, resulting in material wealth and a chance to have lots of children, 'pays', in terms of genes passed on to future generations, for the failure of a lot of left-handed incompetents, who leave few offspring behind.

We make the suggestion slightly tongue in cheek, not least because it suggests, unless we are very careful in our phrasing, that selection is operating 'for the good of society' instead of on individuals. How can our hypothetical left-handed artists do themselves personal good in a right-handed society, enough good to maintain their genes in the population at the ten per cent level?

Well, of course, even the 90 per cent still have active right hemispheres to their brains, hemispheres which appreciate art and music. Although, in Mr Spock's immortal phrase, it is 'not logical' for us to like art and music, almost all of us do, and we are willing to pay for the pleasure it gives us. That payment may represent a manipulation of the majority of the population by the minority in which the right brain dominates.

This does not necessarily mean that all artistis and musicians are left-handed, of course. The genetics are complicated, and more than one gene is at work here, as we have explained. Indeed, some of the complications are present in our own family. One of the authors of this book is right-handed, the other left-handed. But both our children are left-handed (and, incidentally, interested in music). This would be surprising if left-handedness depended on one gene which is present in one of us but not in the other. It is less surprising if we suppose that a combination of several genes makes for left-handedness, and that one of us carries all these genes but the other carries only some – perhaps most – of them.

There may therefore be many people around who carry genes

which make for more effective right-brain activity, without having tipped the balance so far that they are obviously left-handed.

Having done our best to promote left-handers as 'goodies', however, perhaps we should redress the balance. After all, it is possible to explain away their presence in our midst as nothing more nor less than manipulation. They may be like cuckoos in the nest, getting what they need from the more efficient world of left-brain and right-hand dominance, if some current ideas about music are as plausible as they seem.

THE FOOD OF LOVE

Among all the 'artistic' pursuits that give us so much pleasure, but which are, on the face of things, completely useless in evolutionary terms, music is the most interesting, and provides an archetype which we can try to understand as a key to all such phenomena. Nobody can say for certain whether or not other animals experience aesthetic joy at the sight of a beautiful painting or a glorious sunset. But at least some other animals indulge, often at elebaorate length, in what seems to be music – from the song of a nightingale to the honking of a bullfrog. And if we can see some advantage to this behaviour among other animals, some reason why individuals that go in for such things should be winners in the evolutionary stakes, then we shall at least have taken the first steps down the road towards understanding why people like music.

The bullfrog is perhaps a good place to start. There is absolutely no doubt that in his case the 'song' is an advertisement designed to let females know that he is there, and to attract them to him as a mate. The evolutionary advantage of this kind of advertising is clear, and it is also clear that there will be some sort of evolutionary competition between individuals, so that those who carry genes which cause them to produce a song that is more attractive to females will do best and pass on many copies of those genes to future generations.

'Advertisement' is precisely the right word to use to describe this behaviour. In his superb book *The Extended Phenotype*, Richard Dawkins, of the University of Oxford, has elaborated on the theme. Advertisements, he points out, are not designed with the primary object of informing, or misinforming, people. Their primary purpose is to *persuade* people to buy a particular product, to vote a certain way, or whatever. Advertising agencies employ psychologists to advise on the particular things that are likely to appeal to the target group and, equally important, those things to avoid in the advertising campaign for fear of frightening off the audience. Margaret Thatcher, Britain's first woman Prime Minister, achieved that position at least partly because she was advised to change her style of speaking and deepen the tone of her voice in order to become more persuasive. And the entire Presidential career of Ronald Reagan can be taken as a triumph of this combination of advertising and psychological techniques, in the hands of a skilled actor.

This area of psychology is itself fascinating, and deeply involved with human characteristics that have evolved for good, practical reasons out in the forests and plains of Africa, but which may not be quite so obviously useful in modern society. Supermarket managers will tell you, for example, that people like to see large quantities of each item on display in the store. If a shelf has just a few cans on it, they will not sell. This is not necessarily what you would expect – you might anticipate, perhaps, that if only a few cans were on display people would rush to buy them for fear that there would be none left later. But not a bit of it. People rush to buy the things that are piled high in glittering, colourful displays. The same psychology applies to selling books. A book labelled 'the new bestseller' and piled high in a bookstore will sell more effectively than if a few copies are placed on a shelf, even though the shelf may be refilled every time a book is sold.

Advertisers and packagers, the 'hidden persuaders', have been accused of using techniques akin to hypnotism, producing an almost trance-like state in people in supermarkets, so that they end up buying things that are neither wanted nor needed. There is no doubt that cunning psychologists can influence people in this way. By providing both visual and auditory stimuli (bright packaging, big stacks of goods, soft background music, air-conditioned comfort) they lull people into the state they want. The stimuli have a direct effect on the central nervous systems of the individual shoppers, an effect which can actually be monitored by hidden cine-cameras which have been used to count the rate at which passing shoppers blink. Advertising *is* hypnotic.

What has this to do with a frog chorus, or the song of a nightingale? Each frog, says Dawkins, is not just informing the world of his presence. He is advertising, trying to *persuade* all the females that he is the best possible mate. If there are certain sounds, certain frequencies of vibration, that have a hpynotic effect on female frogs, then evolution will quickly favour those male frogs that produce these sounds – and, incidentally, evolution will also select susceptible female frogs to pass their genes on to future generations, since any female that ignores the male chorus and looks elsewhere for a mate is unlikely to leave many offspring. The system has a built-in feedback that perpetuates and reinforces itself. The frog chorus does not have the same effect on people. It is more likely to induce laughter than hypnotic rapture. But the song of the nightingale is another matter entirely. Many people find it so beautifully absorbing that they *do* enter an almost trance-like state, 'as though', as Keats said, 'of hemlock I had drunk'.

The nightingale's song has evolved, of course, to influence other nightingales, not people. It is just a quirk of nature that it should have such a powerful effect on the human nervous system, and we can only imagine the power of its influence over the other nightingales. But we do know that human nervous systems can be strongly influenced by, for example, the appropriate pattern of flashing lights, which can induce trance or epileptic fits. (Incidentally, left-handers are less susceptible to hypnotism than right-handers.) So it would be most surprising if there were no patterns of sound which produced a marked influence on human nervous systems, and it would be truly astonishing if, in that case, people had not evolved an ability to take advantage of this by making sounds which give pleasure to other people. If an individual human being could influence others in this way, the obvious advantage of this ability would be to persuade the others that the person making the sounds is a good person to mate with. After food, finding a mate is the most important thing in life.

Dawkins raises the question of how we would design an 'auditory drug' to induce trance in people – and he promptly answers his own question by suggesting three ingredients: 'the incessant rhythm of an African drum; the eerie trilling of the tree cricket . . . the song of the nightingale.' And, switching from nightingales to another noted songster, the canary, he points out that the song of a male canary is alone sufficent to bring about an enlargement of the ovary of a female canary, and to start her building a nest.

People like to think that they are above such things, superior to the lower animals, but if there is only one per cent difference between ourselves and lesser animals, we may have to accept that we, too, are influenced by such stimuli. Throughout history, successful musicians have been feted and had their pick of potential (and often actual) mates, from Schumann to the Beatles and Michael Jackson. And throughout history the most powerful influence of this kind has been wielded by men, be it Johann Strauss or Paul McCartney. There is ample circumstantial evidence to justify the claim that the ability to make music has evolved in people because it provides successful music makers with an opportunity to influence other people, inducing fear or obedience (as with the drumming associated with witch doctors and black magic), or triggering a sexual response, especially when used by males to manipulate the emotions of young females.

But the manipulation need not be purely sexual. Mickie Most, a pop entrepreneur and manager whose successes included handling Herman's Hermits and The Animals and producing a string of hit records through his own label, has said that 'a good pop song should create an addiction. Hearing it once you can't wait to hear it again. Can't wait, for the next radio play. You have to own it. You have to be able to satisfy that awakened longing whenever you want it satisfied.'[4] Successful musicians today earn money. They manipulate more productive members of our society into providing them with the good things in life. This is a very successful way to behave, *provided* that there are plenty of productive people around for the minority of entertainers to 'feed' off.

So we can make a case that in any human population existing at above the subsistence level there will be room for a minority of individuals to exert an essentially hypnotic influence over the majority, through music or other forms of entertainment or artistic expression, which persuades the majority to provide food, shelter, and reproductive partners for the minority. At least some of the characteristically right-brain activities that we have referred to may provide individual people with a successful way of life simply through giving them a means to influence the nervous systems of other people. In spite of the way in which Paul McCartney lives up to the image we are painting, however, this would not imply that all musicians should be left-handed. We are suggesting that there are degrees of right-brain dominance, linked to several genes, and that 'pure' left-handers represent only the extreme case, the tip of the iceberg. But on this picture there ought to be some stable balance of 'artistic' people, and therefore some constant iceberg-tip proportion of left-handers, in the population. There must be an ESS akin to the hawks vs doves scenario, since, quite clearly, there must be some people around doing productive work, tilling the fields or whatever, to provided food for the cuckoos in their nest. In a population of workers, the cuckoo strategy would be so fantastically successful that genes for the appropriate behaviour would surely spread until the stable balance was struck – even though, just as in the case of hawks and doves, the entire population would undoubtedly have a better standard of living, using the modern terminology, if they all worked productively and shared the fruits of their labours.

How far can the hypothesis be stretched? We have talked in terms of musicians and entertainers as the parasites feeding off productive people, manipulating them by persuasion. But most musicians do, in fact, work quite hard at their trade, even though they do not go out tilling the fields. In every human society, though, there are charming, persuasive rascals who achieve a comfortable lifestyle simply by being charming and persuasive. Is it possible that this is a related form of manipulation? It would not do to press the case too far. Let us stick with the music, where all that we have said can be boiled down into a few words. There are certain sounds which produce a response in the human nervous system that we call pleasure, and we call those sounds music. Therefore, it is no surprise to find that at least some human beings carry a genetic predisposition which enables them to make music and give pleasure to others in return for rewards of one kind or another. It may not sound very romantic, but it does seem that there is no mystery, in evolutionary terms, about Bach's ability to make us happy. Our enjoyment of the Brandenburg Concertos is in no way diminished by this insight, and just possibly we have found a clue to the existence of a minority of left-handers in all human populations.

CHILDHOOD'S END

The last stage in the process of language acquistion comes at adolescence, as a young human being matures into adulthood. Of course, we all continue to learn new words and manners of speech – even new languages – throughout life. But in the turmoil of adolescence there occur the last changes in the fundamental way we use words. Adolescent and post-adolescent speech is, or can be, far more complex than the speech of children. Children's speech tends to be direct and straightforward. When a child wants a favour from a parent, it cannot easily introduce the matter with subtlety, and its idea of low cunning will be to say to father, 'Gee, daddy, isn't that a smart red bicycle? I wish I had a red bicycle.'

Adolescents can be altogether more subtle. They are able to use, with varying degrees of effectiveness at first, such complexities as sarcasm or irony. They can use language to obtain information without asking direct questions on the subject in hand and, if they are good at it, without the person being questioned ever realizing the true purpose of the conversation. This is all-important to a young adolescent trying to find out from a third party, for example, whether a certain member of the opposite sex finds the questioner attractive.

The written language, the use of words and phrases in writing, of adolescents undergoes similar changes. The joke about the young child who writes a letter along the lines 'Dear Aunt Jane, I hope you had a nice birthday. It is my birthday next week. There is a very nice train set in the shop' is amusing to adults precisely because it does reflect the way young children communicate their wishes. An adolescent, although still, perhaps, being more transparent than he or she realizes, will at least make some effort to be more subtle.

So there is a very long process of language acquisition, extending from birth right through to the end of adolescence – 14, 15, even 18 years later. Although there is a long spell of childhood years in which language development primarily consists of learning new words and practising them, the qualitative changes at adolescence make it clear that the whole of childhood is necessary to the development of adult linguistic skills. The long-drawn-out period of childhood, and the long-drawn-out lifespan itself, are uniquely human charcteristics. Language is also a uniquely human characteristic. The two have undoubtedly evolved together. The 'reason' for our long-drawn-out childhood is not simply or solely to give us time to learn to speak, but without the long childhood, and without being born 'unfinished', with a brain that is still developing and capable of learning new tricks, we could not have evolved the kind of linguistic abilities that are so important to human society. Sexual maturity, intellectual maturity, and the ability to communicate in an adult fashion all come together in the adolescent, and combine to make an effective, fully functioning member of human society as childhood ends. But that new adult human being still shares 99 per cent of his or her genetic material with an African ape. In spite of the rich potential for interactions with other people and the world at large provided by that special human heritage of intelligence and speech, our patterns of behaviour still depend, in large measure, on that genetic inheritance we share with the African apes. If we understand that properly, we can use our intelligence and ability as communicators – the one per cent advantage – to overcome the genetic programming, where appropriate, and lift ourselves above the apes. And biologists can shed light on the reasons why we behave as we do by studying that genetic inheritance and by comparing human behaviour with the behaviour of other animals, especially those apes that are such close relations to us. The rules of the game of life are written in our genes, and they are interpreted through a relatively new scientific discipline, called sociobiology.

PART II
THE RULES OF THE GAME

4

IN PRAISE OF SOCIOBIOLOGY

Sociobiology is the study of all forms of social behaviour in all animals, including humans. That sounds innocuous enough, but sociobiology naturally includes the genetic bases of behaviour – a hyena has a very different social life from an albatross, say, and this is fundamentally because the DNA inside the cells of the two species codes for different things. The fact that an albatross has two wings and two legs and is covered by feathers, while a hyena has four legs and no wings and is covered by hair, is due to their different genetic inheritance, and so, clearly, a very large part of sociobiology is about genetic inheritance, which predisposes individual members of different species to do certain things well, and others badly or not at all. Of course, the more interesting aspects of this study concern differences more subtle than those between wings and legs. Why do lions, for example, find it advantageous, in terms of evolutionary success, to form groups (prides) in which one or two males dominate and mate with all the females, while the rest of the males get no chance to reproduce? Why do most birds spend so much time and effort raising their young, while most frogs simply abandon their eggs to take their chance in the world? And so on. The principle is still the same. A bird behaves like a bird, and a frog behaves like a frog, at least partly because of its genetic inheritance.

But when this straightforward line of biological and evolutionary reasoning is applied to humans it causes such a strong reaction in some quarters that the very term 'sociobiology' has become almost a dirty word to a small minority of biologists. The problem does not lie, as you might naively guess, with those who believe in the literal word of the creation story told in the Bible and therefore cannot accept that people should be regarded by science in the same way as other animals. Ironically, the vehement opposition to human sociobiology has come from the other end of the religious spectrum, from self-acknowledged Marxists and atheists who mistakenly believe that sociobiologists are claiming that all human behaviour is so rigidly programmed by our genes that there is little or no scope left for free will.

We would never have dreamed that sociobiology needed singling out for praise (or justification) in this book if it had not been for a lunch-time discussion we attended at the Institute of Contemporary Arts, in London, in 1984. The theme of the discussion was the role of men and women in modern society, and one of us argued that in strict biological terms the human species no longer 'needs' sex, and that both sexual reproduction and males are redundant hangovers from our evolutionary past. (We shall go into all of this in chapter 6.) This drew an almost apoplectic response from one of the other people present, who protested 'But that's blatant sociobiology!' Somewhat baffled, we agreed; of course it was, and is, sociobiology. How else do you study the evolutionary significance of such things as the existence of two sexes in mammals? Our 'opponent' sat back, satisfied. In his eyes, we were condemned out of our own mouths, as sociobiologists, and therefore beyond the pale. Nothing further needed to be said on the matter, and his mind was closed to further discussion.

So, after the meeting, we though we had better find out what all the fuss was about, and why this simple idea of applying sociobiology to humans, which seeemed so straightforward to someone coming into the study of evolution from a training in the physical sciences, should rouse such passions, and be dismissed so strongly, even if those passions only burned in a minority of breasts. And we soon found that the place to start investigating the phenomenon was with the work of Edward Wilson, of Harvard University, who published a landmark book, called *Sociobiology*, in 1975.

What is Sociobiology?

Wilson did not invent the kind of study now called sociobiology, although he was the first to use the word with its present meaning. The roots of investigations into the genetic bases of behaviour of animals (including humans) go back a long way, and some of the key developments in the early 1970s came from Robert Trivers, who is now at the University of California, Santa Cruz. Wilson's best-selling book caused debate, and roused passions (and became a best-seller), because he specifically made the case that people should be treated in the same way, as far as scientific investigations of behaviour are concerned, as other animals. The behaviour of animals is governed, to some extent, by their genes. People are animals. Therefore, the behaviour of people is governed, to some extent, by their genes. The logic seems impeccable, especially when you recall that some 99 per cent of our own genetic material is identical with that of the pygmy chimpanzee. The evolutionary rules that apply to chimps apply to us as well. But still, some people are uncomfortable with that logic, just as many Victorians were unhappy with Charles Darwin's claim that there was *any* biological relationship between mankind and apekind.

In recent years two extreme views have been put forward to explain human behaviour, and much of human history. Konrad Lorenz and Robert Ardrey espoused the view that human beings are driven by innate aggression, genetically determined, which has moulded the development of human society through repeated warfare and which finds an outlet today in activities such as football hooliganism. Ardrey in particular, in a series of best-selling books, promoted the idea that human violence is an inevitable fact of life. B. F. Skinner, on the other hand, has postulated that each newborn human infant is a blank slate, capable of being moulded in any direction depending on the kind of stimuli it receives from the world around it. Train the child to be a warlike aggressor, and you will get an aggressive adult; train the child to be a peaceful farmer, and you will get an adult agriculturalist. As is the case with most extreme views of the world, the truth lies somewhere in between. People are born with certain innate abilities and inclinations, but they are also moulded by their cultural surroundings. We are born with a predisposition to speak, for example, but the language we speak as adults depends on what we hear when we are young.

As we have seen, flexibility, linked with our large brains and long childhoods, is a key human attribute. Lorenz himself argued that, although aggressive behaviour in humans has an innate basis, society might be changed to cope with these basic drives and channel aggression into socially useful forms of behaviour (a different view from Skinner's suggestion that the *child* might be changed to fit society); some of his followers, however, have rather ignored this point. It is interesting to investigate how much of adult behaviour is a result of inheritance ('nature') and how much is due to upbringing ('nurture') – but always remember that the ability to be flexible and adapt is itself something that is part of our genetic inheritance and has evolved because it is successful. During natural selection, *any* device which helps to ensure that a higher proportion of certain genes is passed on to the next generation will become a characteristic feature of the species that carries those genes, and that is why people have the ability to learn new tricks and adapt to different cultural environments, within limits.

If culture were the *overriding* influence on being human, then surely it would be possible to raise a pygmy chimp from birth in a human household and end up with a passable imitation of a human being. In fact, the genetic difference of only one per cent makes this impossible. Humankind is indeed a cultural animal, but our cultural nature and our instincts alike are themselves genetically determined, like our naked skin and our large brains.

The extreme opponents of human sociobiology are concerned that any evidence for a genetic basis for human behaviour will strengthen the case of the Ardreys who argue that human aggression is innate and cannot be controlled. Such biological determinism, in its extreme form, can be, and has been, used as a justification for war, for the domination of society by one class, for the subordinate position of women in society, and for many other evils. We agree wholeheartedly with the opponents of sociobiology that these are indeed evils, which ought to be eradicated from human society. But they are missing the point – sociobiology does *not* presume that our fate is determined by biology in this way. If our behaviour were indeed determined entirely by these kinds of biological imperatives, it would, of course, never occur to us to question them or to regard aggression, rape, racism or the rest as objectionable. They would be perfectly natural to us. The fact that we question such activities is itself conclusive proof that we are not blind victims of genes 'for' aggression, rape, sexism and the rest.

Culture *is* a big influence on human behaviour (thanks to our genes), and we have the intelligence (thanks to evolution) to analyse situations and act on the basis of reasoned argument, instead of by instinct. People are rather *unusual* African apes, and our unusual attributes have to be taken into account. Indeed, what matters is that we should try, through sociobiology, to understand what our animal inheritance predisposes us for, so that we can decide whether that predisposition is good or bad and can take suitable steps to overcome it where necessary. If, for instance, people are innately somewhat aggressive and suspicious of foreigners (possibilities we touch on later in this book) it should be advantageous to understand that and to ensure that we use our intelligence to avoid conflicts.

It seems to us that the position has been best summed up by Wilson himself, writing in *New Scientist*.[1] He said that 'a crucial issue with which sociobiology has to grapple [is]: what are the *relative* [our italics] contributions to human behaviour of genetic endowment and environmental experience? ... we are dealing with a genetically inherited array of possibilities, some of which are shared with other animals, some not, which are then expressed to different degrees depending on environment.'

It is hard to see how any evolutionary biologist can take exception to such a statement. It is true, unfortunately, that extreme right-wing groups have misused some of the ideas in sociobiology as a 'justification' for racism, claiming that biology 'proves' some people to be inferior to others. What seems to have happened is that extreme left-wing groups have mistaken this abuse of sociobiology by their bitterest foes for the real thing, and have not taken time to appreciate what researchers such as Wilson and Trivers are really saying. Discarding sociobiology because a few neo-Nazis claim that it implies that certain races are inferior is like banning the manufacture of knives because a few people commit murders with them. What we mean by sociobiology is precisely summed up in the passage quoted from Wison's *New Scientist* article. And a great deal has happened since 1976 to put sociobiology in general, and human sociobiology in particular, on a footing so secure that no blasts of hot air can shake it.

SOCIOBIOLOGY TODAY

John Krebs, of the University of Oxford, has summed up the major themes that have emerged as sociobiology developed in the years following publication of Wison's book.[2] The most important development is the introduction of games theory into the study of evolution, with the idea of ESS – a concept so basic and informative, indeed, that we have already used it, without waiting to go into the nitty gritty of what sociobiology is all about. This underpins most of the rest of this book. Two themes that are related to each other are the puzzle of why individuals should so often be willing to cooperate with one another – as in the cooperative social life of a pride of lions – and why there is competition and disharmony even within such cooperative groups, as when the dominant male is supplanted by a younger rival, who promptly kills all the infant cubs in the pride. The roots of this kind of behaviour, both cooperation and competition, can be found in the concept of the 'selfish gene', the argument that the actual units of natural selection are the genes themselves, even though selection has, perforce, to operate (like the genes) on whole bodies.

This idea is important enough, especially when linked with the ESS idea, to merit a little further discussion. It was presented most forcefully by Richard Dawkins, also of Oxford University, in his popular book *The Selfish Gene*, and he has developed the theme further in his even better book *The Extended Phenotype*, where he replies to earlier criticism and, in our view, thoroughly confounds the arguments of his critics, while developing the selfish gene concept more completely and more clearly. Dawkins argues that bodies – phenotypes – exist primarily because they are the means by which genes ensure their own replication, and should be viewed as such if we are to understand the workings of evolution. In the words of the biological aphorism, a hen is simply the egg's way of making more eggs. Or, in human terms, a person is simply the genes' way to manufacture more copies of themselves.

Life on Earth is all about replication – copying – of strands of DNA. The complexity of life we see around us, including our own species, is a result of competition and selection which has produced a variety of different ways to ensure the copying of DNA, and has produced many kinds of DNA – many genes – along the way. This is a blind process operating in accordance with the laws of physics and chemistry, and statistics, with no guiding intelligence behind it, as one of us has described in *In Search of the Double Helix*. But with that clearly understood, it is often convenient to anthropomorphize somewhat and to use everyday expressions to discuss how the genes ensure their replication. We may say, for example, that a gene 'wants' to ensure that copies of itself get spread among subsequent generations. Obviously one effective way to do this is to 'help' the body in which it lives to reproduce and leave many offspring behind. That is basic Darwinian evolution; genes that make a body better fitted to its environment will inevitably be selected for and will spread. But this is not the full story. Because of the way genes are inherited, half from each parent, there is a 50:50 chance that two offspring who share the same two parents will have any one of their genes in common. On average, half the genes of full siblings will be identical in each body, each phenotype. Or, from the 'point of view' of a particular gene residing in the cells of one body, there is a 50:50 chance that the cells of the body of a sibling carry copies of the same gene.* So, if one sibling helps another to find food, or a mate, and, ultimately, to reproduce, then he or she is helping to ensure the spread of very many of the genes that are in his or her own body. If a gene arises which causes the body it inhabits to behave in such a way that the survival of siblings is encouraged – even if this is merely a side effect of whatever influence the gene has on the phenotype – then the gene will spread, because half the siblings carry

---

* We are using the term 'gene' a little loosely here, where our more rigorous biological friends would prefer the term 'allele'; we believe our meaning is clear, and hope they will forgive us. Perhaps we should also clear up another potential source of confusion. Humans and chimps share 99 per cent of their DNA, in the sense that the human 'recipe' (or blueprint) is 99 per cent the same as the chimp recipe. Two siblings (of either species) may share 50 per cent of their DNA, in the sense that they have many identical alleles. What the 50 per cent of the DNA actually shares is a common immediate origin, by being derived from the same original DNA parent. In fact, a great deal of the DNA inherited from each parent will be the same. The basic recipe for having, for example, two legs and two eyes is in all human DNA (and all chimp DNA), and such subtleties as whether the eyes are brown or blue occupy only a tiny fraction of the whole genetic code. Although half the DNA comes from each parent, the vast majority of it is the *same* in each parent, and specifies things like having two legs and two eyes and how to manufacture haemoglobin. The discussion here relates to the minority of genes that come in two or more versions and which affect our behaviour.

the same gene – assuming, for simplicity, that the gene has no harmful effect on its own phenotype. The mathematics of ESS can handle such subleties, though, and in the simple case, if the benefit to siblings is more than twice the handicap resulting to the carrier of the gene, then the gene ought to spread, since with a 50:50 chance of the gene being present in the siblings the benefits *to copies of the gene* will outweigh the handicap *to one individual phenotype*. At a stroke, this concept explains, in a qualitative way, why close relations should cooperate with one another – and, indeed, members of a pride of lions will, in general, be relatives. The mathematics of population genetics can put numbers into the calculations, and when this is done the combination of the idea of selfish genes and games theory can very often account for otherwise puzzling biological phenomena.

One very simple example demonstrates the power of this approach and shows how sociobiology has stood the test of time. This kind of cooperative behaviour would be useless if individuals had no way to recognize their close relatives. So it is a requirement of sociobiology that close relations, especially full siblings, should be able to identify each other. This is not something that emerges naturally from any other version of evolutionary ideas, and it was not anticipated even as recently as 1970. But studies by Paul Sherman, of Cornell University, of the behaviour of a creature known as Belding's ground squirrel have shown that these animals distinguish between littermates that are full siblings and those that are half siblings, having the same mother but a different father. The ground squirrels behave differently towards each type of relation – their social life is moulded by biology. It does not matter *how* the distinction is made (though we might guess that smell has something to do with it). What matters is that it occurs at all.

This is, of course, an example of the way that we are taught that science ought to work. A new hypothesis is aired and used to make a testable prediction. When the test is carried out, we decide whether or not the hypothesis is a good one, worth elevating to the status of a theory, according to the outcome of the test. In this sense, sociobiology is established as a set of good working hypotheses, or a scientific theory, unless and until it has to be modified, or replaced by a better theory, when it fails some future test of this kind. Wilson himself prefers to regard sociobiology as a scientific discipline, like physics, say, and in that sense the whole of sociobiology is not a scientific theory and not testable in the same sense. Instead, it *contains* many testable hypotheses and theories within itself. But just as the success of Newton's laws helps to give us confidence in the whole structure of physics, so the success of this particular prediction helps to give us confidence in the whole basis of sociobiology.

Since 1975, the sociobiological approach has also led to a better understanding of reproductive strategies among animals, how mates are chosen and why some species are monogamous while others are not, and to investigation of different strategies for care of the young, such as the difference between birds and frogs mentioned earlier. Why, for instance, is there a roughly equal balance between males and females in our own species? And a close cousin of games theory, called optimization theory, can, as Krebs explains, correctly predict '*exactly how much time* an individual will spend searching for food or mates in a particular place'. Finally, for our present purposes, sociobiology has opened up another fruitful line of investigation, asking the question of how much it benefits an individual to transfer information to others, either through its displays or through its vocal calls or songs. Giving away information is likely to be a bad strategy. In our example of the mythical hawks vs doves scenario, for example, when two 'doves' are involved in staring each other down the worst thing to do would be to hint that you were about to cut and run. The new view of animal behaviour suggests that many signals are designed (that is, have evolved by natural selection) to provide *mis*information, to persuade, like advertisements. And since a deliberate liar can be unconvincing, the best way to mislead others may well involve the individual making the display 'believing' in it – the dove that is about to cut and run really does not know, until the last instant, that this is going to happen.

There are also important new insights into evolution at work to be gained from the application of sociobiology, including the concept of selfish genes and the use of games theory, to the world of plants. But we have more than enough here to chew on already, and anyone interested in following up all the new avenues of research can seek out Wilson's books and others cited in the bibliography. Here, we want to concentrate on animals, particularly mammals, and specifically human beings. Four key features of human behaviour need to be explained by any good theory of evolution. The evolution of cooperation, or altruism, was for decades the most puzzling problem of all, and as we shall see in the next chapter the explanation of altruism was the success that laid the foundation stone of sociobiology. Apart from finding enough to eat, the fundamental requirement for all life, the three key sociological issues involving people are then the problem of sex (how to find a mate, and what to do once you have found one), the need not just to mate and dump the offspring to fend for themselves (like many frogs) but to care for and nurture the young (a problem particularly acute for human beings, with their long childhood) and the thorny problem of just how much innate aggression we really do carry 'in our genes'. Those issues, and the sociobiology that underpins the human variations on the three themes, form the basis of part III of this book. But before we get on to the meat of our message, there is one lesser issue which has roused great passions from time to time during the past hundred years or so, and which provides a nice case study of what sociobiology is and is not about. This is the question of intelligence.

INTELLIGENCE AND EVOLUTION

You might think, to read some of the writings of the biological left, that sociobiology fails as a scientific discipline simply because it cannot account for the present variability of human intelligence (as revealed by standard tests) in purely genetic terms – that it has, in a sense, failed the intelligence test.[3] But far from it.

Intelligence is one of those concepts which, like time, is impossible to define satisfactorily. We all know what intelligence is, just as we all know what time is, but none of us can put the concept down properly in words. This is the root cause of all the misunderstanding about intelligence, which has not been helped by the unfortunate use of the term 'intelligence quotient', or IQ, to describe an ability of the human brain that is tested by IQ tests. What ability is tested in this way? Only the ability of individuals to do IQ tests – a skill which is certainly related to 'real' intelligence but is very far from the whole story, as we shall see. But before plumbing those murky depths, one thing should be clear. Unless you believe that God (or some godlike visitor similar to the ones in the film *2001*) was responsible for making the changes in our DNA that distinguish us from pygmy chimpanzees, or Belding's ground squirrel, or an ant, then it is clear that human intelligence, the most important aspect of being human, has been produced by evolution through the process of natural selection. As we have seen, this depends on two things. First, characteristics are inherited by individual members of a species from the individual's parents – we now know, through the replication and passing on of genes, bits of DNA. Secondly, there is a variation among the individual members of a species. Natural selection then operates because the individuals that are better fitted to their environment will be more successful, and will pass on more copies of their genes than those individuals whose phenotypes are less well fitted to their environment.

This applies to every characteristic that has evolved, from the relative length of your arms and your legs, to the innate human ability for language, to the efficiency of the haemoglobin in your blood as a transporter of oxygen. Of course, there may be characteristics, such as different eye colours, which are neutral, conferring no particular evolutionary advantage or disadvantage and not subject to much in the way of selection, but few would argue that intelligence falls into that category. (We are not saying that eye colour *is* selectively neutral, only that it *might be*.) We are more intelligent than our ancestors, and we owe our success as a species in very large measure to that intelligence. Clearly, intelligence has evolved. Therefore, equally clearly, intelligence is something that is inherited. Certainly until the emergence of modern man, *Homo sapiens*, individuals with above-average intelligence *must* have produced children with above-average intelligence, and they must have been more successful in raising those children, so that the genes 'for' intelligence spread through the population in succeeding generations. At the same time, less intelligent individuals must have been producing less intelligent children, and those children must have been less successful, in each generation, than their more intelligent rivals. If this had not been the case, intelligence in the form that we possess it today would not have evolved. The selection pressure may not have been strong, and the differences involved may have been small – after all, they took millions of years to turn *Homo habilis* into *Homo sapiens*. But undoubtedly they did exist. Whether they still exist, and whether they operate in the same way today, is perhaps open to doubt. The human species now controls the environment to such an extent that characteristics that would cause individuals to be at a disadvantage even 50 000 years ago, let alone 5 million years ago, are not 'selected against' in the old way. In many ways, it is no longer a question of fitting ourselves to the environment but rather one of fitting the environment to us. But the line of argument we have just outlined provides a very strong suggestion, to say the least, that human intelligence is an inherited characteristic that has a degree of variability within the human population. Even so, although the semantics may be confusing, that is not at all what the often heated 'IQ debate' has been about.

THE INTELLIGENCE TEST

Between 1924 and 1972 some 7500 American citizens were sterilized by doctors acting on government orders, without the patients being told what was happening to them. The scandal only came to light in 1980; it was based on a misconception of the nature of intelligence and heredity that was unfounded in the 1920s, and had long been *proved* to be unfounded by the time this government-approved 'breeding programme' was halted. In every case, the victims were people regarded as mentally deficient, and many were themselves the offspring of parents with low intelligence. The pseudo-scientific basis for the sterilization programme can be summed up in the words of one Supreme Court Judge in 1927 – 'three generations of imbecility is plenty'.

You would think, from that, that there was a proven basis for the assumption that the overwhelmingly dominant factor in determining the intelligence of an individual is the intelligence of that person's parents. And yet, ironically, this attitude was fostered by the misuse of a system for measuring intelligence that originated, in France, from evidence for the exact opposite, that the important factor in determining the intelligence of an adult human being is the way that person has been raised. Nurture, not nature, determines the extent to which the intellectual potential inherent in *all* healthy members of *Homo sapiens* is achieved.

Ideas about intelligence have tended to reflect the times. In the nineteenth century, the common belief (in Europe and the United States, at least) was that the white races were superior and destined to rule the world, while, closer to home, it went without saying that men were more intelligent than women. Paul Broca, whom we have already met, was a great one for measuring the size of any brain he could lay his hands on, and even he usually managed to delude himself into believing that the measurements supported his preconceptions. The average weight of a human brain is about 1450 g, so Broca was pleased to find that the famous Russian novelist Turgenev had a brain weighing more than 2000 g, while the zoologist Cuvier had a brain weighing 1830 g. The discovery that the great mathematician Gauss had a brain weight of only 1492 g was a little disappointing, and Broca could never know, of course, that his own brain weighed a mere 1424 g. But the way in which expectation moulds our view of the world is best shown by his study of the brains of several German professors, late of Göttingen University. Finding that some of them were relative lightweights, in brain size, he wrote 'the title of Professor does not necessarily guarantee genius'. He could, of course, have concluded that being a genius does not depend upon having a large brain!

Broca's attitude to women similarly reflected the culture of his era. He noted that women have, on average, smaller brains than men (the difference is about 180 g) and commented 'we must not forget that women are on average less intelligent than men' – not *totally* failing to point out that women are, on average, smaller than men, but continuing 'the relatively small size of the female brain partly reflects her smaller physique and partially her intellectual inferiority'. In fact, as Broca could easily have calculated, the smaller physique alone is more than enough to account for the smaller brain size in women. But, as we know, brain size is not simply correlated with intelligence; it is the quality of the brain, not just the quantity, that counts.

Similar prejudices shine through in other studies of the supposed intelligence of underpriviliged groups, such as blacks, in nineteenth-century studies. There is no point in elaborating on them here, for the attitude to women, expressed by Broca, is entirely representative of the times. So it came as a shaft of scientific light amongst the gloom of all these preconceptions when the Frenchman Alfred Binet tackled the problem of 'backward' schoolchildren in the early 1900s.

Binet was working with children who had learning problems. Such children could not benefit from the standard teaching programme in the schools of the educational system of Paris, and the initial problem facing Binet was to devise a test which could weed out these misfits and ensure that the rest of the children proceeded smoothly with their education. But why were some children backward? Binet argued that the problem was not that they were innately stupid but that, for one reason or another, their intelligence had not been brought out, and had failed to develop. Once Binet's early intelligence test had located a child with 'low intelligence', the obvious thing to do was to provide the child with a special educational programme in order to exercise his or her intellectual skills and enable the infant to catch up with other children of the same age. Just as a physically underdeveloped child could be given a programme of athletics and weight-training exercises to build up the body, so, Binet reasoned, a mentally underdeveloped child could be given equivalent mental training.

Binet's test started out from the assumption that older children should be able to carry out mental tasks that younger ones cannot, and he decided on the 'normal' level of achievement for each age group by discussing the children's abilities with their school teachers. He developed a simple test that produced scores, when those children were tested, in close agreement with the estimate of the teachers regarding the relative intelligence of the children in their charge, and then used the test to identify children who were two or more years 'behind' their age mates and needed special tuition. And Binet's ideas were supported by evidence that came from Belgium when his test was first used there. Children in a Belgian school were found to have much higher 'mental ages' than the children in Paris – exactly what should have been expected, said Binet, since the Belgian children were attending a private school with small classes, and showed the benefits compared with the Paris children from larger schools with much bigger classes and less individual attention from teachers.

The Binet test, first published in 1905, should have ushered in a new era of educational enlightenment. Instead, in being translated and adapted for use in the English speaking world it became an instrument used to support the old nineteenth-century preconceptions about intelligence.

Binet himself died young, in 1911, and was not around to protest at the transformations wreaked on his test, and its misapplications. In the United States, the test was translated and adapted by Lewis Terman, of Stanford University, who introduced what became known as the 'Stanford–Binet' test of IQ in 1916. This was, basically, the test used to determine the fate of hundreds of thousands of people in the United States over the next half century, together with a similar test devised by US psychologist Robert Yerkes. The tests perpetrated such inanities that it is hard to see, looking back from the 1980s, how they were ever taken seriously. Polish immigrants, with no knowledge of American language or customs, were classified as having a low IQ partly because they were unable to name famous baseball stars (we kid you not); illiterates, who could not take a written test, were assessed by, among other things, being shown a picture of a tennis court with the net missing and being asked to complete the picture. Apart from the fact that many had never held a pencil before, many had never seen a tennis court in their lives. Result – a score of zero, and another imbecile goes on the list. Thanks largely to these tests, it was officially decided that Poles and Italians were geneticaly inferior to other would-be immigrants and too stupid to be allowed admittance to the United States. And at a time when many were desperate to escape from the rising tide of Fascism and Nazism in Europe, in the 1930s the doors of America were closed to them. Quite literally, innocent people died because of the Stanford–Binet and Yerkes tests.

In England, the Binet test was enthusiastically taken up, and misused, by Cyril Burt, to such effect that late in life he received a knighthood for his contributions to remodelling the British educational system. Burt was largely responsible for the iniquitous 'eleven plus' system (which we both benefited from, but which was no less iniquitous for that) whereby children were tested, with a kind of Binet test, at about age 11. No account was taken of background or of the kind of environmental opportunities of the children. As a result of that one series of test they were labelled as having a certain intelligence, and those with a score higher than an arbitrary cutoff point were selected for the advantages of a 'good' education leading towards public examinations and, hopefully, to university. One of his aims, to be sure, was to bring through the system into higher education children who were intellecutally able but came from a class background which would have deprived them of educational opportunities. That seems laudable enough, but the rest were dumped into second-class schools where they received fewer opportunities and, hardly surprisingly, achieved less. This was the exact opposite of Binet's approach. He would have said, it now seems correctly, that the children who 'failed' such a test should have been given special attention, and that as a result they would then very probably have achieved, in due course, as much as those who had 'passed' the test.

Burt's case is a sad one of self-delusion, based on preconceptions so extreme that they led him, researchers discovered after his death, to invent data and publish fictitious scientific papers under false names (sometimes in journals he edited). The papers were entirely made up out of his own head, to back up his ideas. He did not intend to mislead, of course, but simply could not be bothered to do the research, because he 'knew' what answers it would give. Nobody checked up on him, in the 1950s, because 'everyone knew' that IQ was an absolute, a fixed, unchangeable number carried by individuals throughout life. Unfortunately, that is still popular mythology, and education in Britain is still suffering the consequences, although at least the eleven plus has now gone. Even so, as recently as 1973 psychologist Hans Eysenck could be found making the claim, described by Nobel Laureate Peter Medawar as 'the silliest remark I have ever heard', that 'the whole course of development of a child's intellectual capabilities is largely laid down genetically'.[4]

One of us is a teacher, and has seen firsthand how the myth typified by Eysenck's remark can still warp lives. Time and again children in schools in the 1980s are labelled as virtually unteachable, and in overcrowded classrooms are largely ignored and left to amuse themselves as best they can while harassed teachers concentrate on teaching the majority as much as they can. Yet, in our experience, every time that such an 'unteachable' child has been singled out for attention, he or she has blossomed, soon catching up to the point where there is some hope of including him or her in the routine classwork, and often going on, having discovered unsuspected abilities, to become one of the class leaders. With classes of 30 or more children, there is a limit to what can be achieved without neglecting the other children. But in an ideal world where children were taught in groups of four or five, each group receiving the full attention of a teacher, then, our own experience suggests, Binet's expectations would be amply fulfilled.

Many, many genuine studies, including those of adopted children, of children in orphanages, of twins raised apart and together, all point to the same conclusion today. Given the right environment and mental stimulation from infancy, any child will score well on a Binet test by the age of 11, and will grown up to be an intelligent adult. It is an indictment of society, not genes, that so many children today fail to achieve their potential. And this brings up right back to the heart of what sociobiology is all about.

SOCIOBIOLOGY, HEREDITY, AND INTELLIGENCE

Human sociobiology is *not* about subtle differences between one human being and another. Whether Steve Ovett can run a mile faster than Steve Cram (or whether either can run it faster than the authors of this book) is not a matter for sociobiological debate. What *is* interesting is that both these great athletes, and both the authors of this book, and all other members of the species *Homo sapiens*, do their running on two legs, not on all fours. In other words, the comparisons that should be made are those between *Homo sapiens* and other species. Sociobiology may help us to understand why the chimpanzee lifestyle is successful under certain conditions, why frogs in general do well in the kind of environment frogs inhabit, and why people are so successful *compared with other species*. From this perspective, we see immediately that intelligence is a huge advantage for *Homo sapiens*, and we see that it is an inherited characteristic that has evolved markedly over the past five million years or so. We see that *all* normal human beings inherit the capacity to be quite astonishingly intelligent compared with all other species on Earth, even the chimpanzees. Even a human being from a deprived environment is much, much smarter than the brightest chimpanzee, and *that* is what sociobiology is all about.

Of course, there are variations in intelligence, just as some people are bigger than others and some run faster than others. The occasional genius, like Albert Einstein, is offset, in the statistics, by the occasional moron. But by and large every individual human being has the innate capacity to be as intelligent as any other, just as we are all born with the innate capacity to become fluent linguists. Very many people grow up with stunted linguistic skills because they are brought up in almost inarticulate surroundings; very many people (often the same people) grow up with stunted mental skills, because they grow up in intellectually stunted surroundings. But the lesson we learn *from sociobiology* is that if society cared to provide the proper opportunities for all its citizens, then they would all develop to what is nowadays regarded as a high standard of intelligence.

It is supremely ironic that the abuses of the Stanford–Binet and Yerkes tests, and the work of Cyril Burt, are among the key factors which have led Marxists, whose creed is one of equality, to attack the whole concept of human sociobiology. Genetics and sociobiology tell us that human beings are indeed created very nearly equal, just as the Declaration of Independence tells us, sharing the vast majority of their DNA, and each with the potential to achieve great things, as athletes, musicians, linguists, mathematicians or whatever, depending on the very slight natural preferences they may have to go in one direction or another, and, crucially, on the opportunities they are given to develop those innate abilities. And this unitary view of humanity is the underlying theme of the whole of sociobiology, and of the rest of this book. When we look at the relationship between parents and children, for example, we are not concerned with the question of whether Mrs Jones is a 'better' mother than Mrs Brown; we are interested in finding out why any human mother should be 'willing' to devote so much time and effort to raising a helpless infant – how could such a system have evolved? When we look at sex, we are not really bothered about whether Mr Jones is a more faithful husband than Mr Brown; we want to know why human beings pair up in marriage, why there shoud be two sexes, and why there should be equal numbers of men and women around. When we look at aggression, we are not going to puzzle over the question of whether one individual or another is a violent person; instead we shall look at the overall patterns of human aggressive behaviour. And when we puzzle over the nature of altruism, in the next chapter, we are not going to worry about whether or not one person is kinder than another. Of course there are variations within the whole population, just as there are with most inherited characteristics. The really interesting thing is that people have worked together so effectively, over the generations, that we have come to dominate the planet in less than ten thousand years since the invention of civilization. How can this be squared with the notion of old fashioned Darwinism, with individuals struggling for survival and for scarce resources in fierce competition with other individual members of the same species? And how does altruism fit in with the 'selfish genery' of Richard Dawkins? The simplistic interpretation of those ideas leads you to expect that every man will be out for himself, every woman likewise, and devil take the hindmost. The surprising thing is that the great majority of people are so nice to each other – but sociobiology can tell us why.

5

PEOPLE ARE QUITE NICE, REALLY

Fitness, in the Darwinian sense, is measured by the success of an individual in reproducing – in passing on copies of its genes to the next generation. Strictly speaking, the only way to compare the relative evolutionary success of two individual members of the same species is to wait until both of them have died, and then to count up the number of offspring they have left behind to reproduce in their turn. The more surviving offspring, the more 'fit' the individual was.

For species like our own, with two sexes, there obviously has to be some minimal degree of cooperation between two individuals – a man and a woman – in order to reproduce at all. This vital aspect of being human is the first topic we are going to look at in detail in part III of this book. But, apart from the necessity of finding a breeding partner, naive Darwinism might lead you to expect individuals to be always in conflict, often violent conflict, with other members of their own species. Although a lion cannot really be said to be in competition with, say, a swift, since they occupy quite different ecological niches, a lion must be in very real competition with other lions since they live in the same parts of the world, eat the same kind of food, and even need to find the same kind of mates. Close evolutionary relations ought to be most competitive, on this simple picture, because their needs are very similar and they 'ought' therefore to be fighting over the available resources.

Against this picture of naive Darwinism, the fact that people sometimes act aggressively towards one another, and that human history is dotted with conflicts, is no surprise at all. But it is absolutely astonishing that we are able to cooperate with one another, and that we band together in tribes, cities, nations and other sociological groups to work, by and large, for the common good. We are, indeed, civilized. Although many scientists and popularizers have made much of the aggressive side of human nature, this remains the exception to the general rule, which is why it is newsworthy (how often do you hear on the news about an old lady who walked down the street without being mugged?), and it is fascinating to us largely because it is *not* 'normal' everyday behaviour. Biologists will tell you that humans do not, in fact, rank very high on the scale of fighting, aggressive mammals. There are many more vicious hunters than ourselves, and several species where conflict between individuals is much more common and bloody – even deer, in spite of our cosy image of cuddly Bambi, go in for spectacular combats at certain times of the year. No, there is no getting away from it. People are quite nice, really. But why?

In his *New Scientist* article in 1976, Edward Wilson singled out altruism as 'a central theoretical problem in sociobiology'. Altruism is defined very carefully by biologists. An altruistic act is one that gives a benefit to one individual at a cost to another, and it is measured in reproductive terms, so that an altruistic individual is one that reduces its own reproductive success in order to enhance the reproductive success of another individual or other individuals. The extreme examples of this are found in social insects, such as bees, where there are whole casts of sterile workers who never reproduce at all but spend their lives ensuring that the queen breeds successfully. This behaviour is now very well explained in terms of genes and sociobiology, as we shall see. But in more general terms altruism can extend right up to the level of just plain being nice to people – loving thy neighbour, in fact. Individuals have evolved through billions of years of natural selection, and only characteristics that are advantageous in terms of evolutionary fitness (or, at the very least, confer no evolutionary burden) will survive the winnowing process. We share 99 per cent of our DNA with other animals, and our 'niceness' must have been selected for; by some measures, we are the most successful species on Earth, and there is every reason to think that our niceness is a major contributor to that success. If we did not cooperate, we would reduce our own numbers so effectively that other species would have more opportunities. It looks as if the natural aggression and competition that the simplest version of Darwinism predicts has been suppressed by some mechanism which acts for the benefit of the species, or of a large group of individuals. This is a superficially appealing idea which still appears from time to time in some popular accounts of evolution. But group selection was knocked on the head, as a scientific theory, in the early 1960s.

Ironically, but in the best traditions of the scientific method, group selection was clearly seen to be inadequate as a description of evolution at work once one painstaking scientist had carried out a thorough analysis and published a comprehensive review supporting the group selection hypothesis. Once the hypothesis was laid out logically, other researchers were able to pinpoint the flaws in the argument which led to a revival of the strict Darwinian view that selection operates on individuals, and this was a major influence in the rise of sociobiology. The difference from Darwin's day, however, is that we can now see the importance of genes – which were unknown to Darwin – to the evolutionary story. Individual phenotypes will behave in such a way that they maximize the chance of copies of the genes that they carry being passed on to the next generation, whether those genes come from their own bodies or from those of another member of the same species. Richard Dawkins' image of the 'extended phenotype' is the modern version – gene selection – which sees members of a group cooperating because they share many genes in common. But the perspective is exactly the opposite of the original group selectionists, starting out now from the smallest reproductive units and working upwards, instead of starting out from the species and breaking it down into individuals.

THE GROUP SELECTION FALLACY

It is worth taking a quick look at the ideas of group selection, since an understanding of the flaws in the argument leads almost inevitably to an understanding of how natural selection really does work. The definitive statement of group selection ideas was made by the Scot V. C. Wynne-Edwards, in his book *Animal Dispersion in Relation to Social Behaviour*, in 1962. Wynne-Edwards argued that animals have a natural tendency to avoid over exploiting their habitats. In particular, he said, individuals have some means of recognizing how much food there is to go around, and then, for the good of the species as a whole, they will hold back their reproduction, or even give it up altogether, to avoid overpopulation. In this picture, a great deal of social behaviour was thought to stem from the need for individuals to be kept informed of the population density – the gathering of flocks of birds, or herds of deer, for example, was supposed to allow individuals to assess the numbers and adjust their own reproductive activity accordingly.

The counter to this line of argument in terms of individual selection is very straightforward. Just as in the hawks vs doves scenario, imagine a single mutant individual occurring in a large group of, say, birds. Every other member of the group might be a good, well-behaved group selectionist, busy counting up the size of the flock and deciding that there are too many individuals around this year so it would be best not to lay any (or many) eggs. The mutant, however, has no such qualms. It sets out to rear as many offspring as it can. Some of those offspring will carry the same inherited tendency to maximize their own reproduction, regardless of the good of the group, and the genetic package that makes for this behaviour will spread rapidly in succeeding generations. The mathematics of Maynard Smith's games theory confirms what ought to be intuitively obvious, that the mutant behaviour soon becomes the dominant pattern – the ESS in this case, as in almost every other case, is to rear as many offspring as possible at all times.

This does not mean, for a bird, laying as many eggs as possible at all times. Studies of the English great tit, for example, have shown that, although the typical clutch of eggs numbers nine or ten, some birds lay fewer and some as many as 12 or 13 eggs. But under normal environmental conditions (average weather, and so on) the largest number of nestmates that survive to be fledged from the nest always come from the nests with nine or ten eggs to start with. If there are too many offspring for the parents to feed adequately, the weakest fail to reach maturity.

There are also problems with group selection ideas when we look at the evolutionary process. Evolution by natural selection depends on the difference in reproduction between the successful and the less successful. According to the group selection hypothesis, that means that more successful *groups* have to be selected for, while less successful groups die out. This is difficult enough to arrange in any mathematical model (let alone a plausible one); it becomes virtually impossible to arrange if we consider the possibility that when a group is facing extinction, for whatever reason, then natural selection will strongly favour any individuals who move away from the threat and continue the existence of the species elsewhere.

In the 1980s, the balance of evidence clearly supports the original idea of individual selection rather than the group selection hypothesis. Robert Trivers has summed up four key points against Wynne-Edwards's ideas;[1] they can be paraphrased like this:

1 There are no known patterns of behaviour that cannot be explained more easily in terms of natural selection of individuals, so group selection is unnecessary.
2 Outside influences, such as food shortages or predators, control the numbers of a species present in any region without the kind of 'group altruism' required by Wynne-Edwards, and without the kind of group extinctions required if selection were acting at the level of the group.
3 Since the early 1960s, many studies of the breeding success of individuals – their evolutionary fitness – have been carried out, and they *always* show that animals adopt the strategy of reproducing as rapidly as circumstances permit.
4 Although mathematical games can be set up where group selection operates, it is always a weak effect which is at the mercy of the arrival on the scene of a mutant individual acting in its own self-interest. Group selection *never* provides an ESS.

In the world today, and throughout the vast bulk of evolutionary history, all new traits must appear in rare members of a species, says Trivers, and will increase in frequency among the members of the population only if they increase the survival prospects and reproductive success of the *individuals* that carry the new traits.

Darwin up to Date

Even what seems to be altruism, operating at the level of individuals, or phenotypes, is really selfishness, operating at the level of genes. The important feature of reproduction, in evolutionary terms, is not that a human being gives birth to another human being, or that a wasp hatches out from a wasp egg. What matters is that DNA is being copied, and a gene is the basic unit involved in that process. The argument is most familiar today through the widespread success of Richard Dawkins' book *The Selfish Gene*. It was actually put on a secure mathematical footing in the early 1960s (ironically, at about the same time, but with far less immediate attention, that Wynne-Edwards's ideas on group selection were publicized), by William D. Hamilton, and the basic concepts had already been aired by the mathematician R. A. Fisher and by J. B. S. Haldane. Selfish genery is Darwinism at its simplest, and, in its latest form, Darwinism at its most up to date.

'Traditional' Darwinism sees evolution acting upon individual phenotypes, which are the units of selection. It is in this sense that altruism is a puzzle, because it is not immediately obvious why an individual should help another individual to reproduce at the cost of reducing his or her own chances of reproduction. The blindingly simple solution to this puzzle – a very real puzzle before the genetic mechanism of heredity was understood – comes from looking at close relations and at their common genetic inheritance. The closest relations are parents and their offspring, and full siblings (brothers and sisters who share the same parents), so that is the best place to start.

In a sense, even parental behaviour is a form of altruism, especially in a species like our own where infants are so helpless for so long. Of course, it is obvious why care of helpless infants should have evolved – if we do not look after our own children, we have very little prospect of passing on our genes to succeeding generations. Especially before the invention of civilization, genes that lead people to be good parents will survive, while those that make for individuals that neglect babies will not. And it is by extending this idea that we can arrive at an understanding of altruism in general.

We might as well think in human terms here, although what we have to say applies to any species that reproduces in the way we do.

Each new human being has a unique genotype (excluding the special cases of identical twins, triplets and so on) which is made up of a combination of genes inherited from each parent. In most cases, the mother and father are not close relations, so we can regard each of them as having an independent set of the possible genes (strictly speaking, alleles) available in the human gene pool. Half of their child's genes come from each parent, so geneticists say that there is a relatedness of $\frac{1}{2}$ between a child and either of its parents. The same simple rule applies to all children and all parents – the relatedness between father and daughter, mother and son, mother and daughter and father and son is always $\frac{1}{2}$. What about the children's relatedness to each other?

All children of the same mother inherit half her genes. But they do not all inherit the same genes from her. It is possible that two of her children may inherit copies of almost exactly the same half-set of genes, and therefore have very similar genotypes; equally, it is possible that one may inherit half her genes and the other may inherit the other half, reducing the relatedness. On average, though, there is a 50:50 chance that one of the genes copied and passed on to one child will also be passed on to its sibling. So, on average, half the genes that each child inherits from the mother will be the same as those in any other child that has the same mother. And, since half the total genotype is provided by the mother, that means that, on average, siblings that share the same mother have a relatedness of $\frac{1}{4}$ (half of one-half). Exactly the same reasoning applies to siblings who share the same father. So for full siblings, which share *both* parents, we simply add up the two contributions to find that their relatedness is, on average, $\frac{1}{2}$ – the same as the relatedness of parent to offspring.

It is very simple to extend this argument to other relations. The next closest kin, after siblings and parents, are full cousins. You share half your genes with your mother who, on average, shares half her genes with her sister who, in turn, shares half her genes with her daughter. So the probability that you and your cousin share any one gene is $\frac{1}{2} \times \frac{1}{2} \times \frac{1}{2}$, or $\frac{1}{8}$. This kind of calculation immediately puts a new complexion on Darwinian evolution.

If an individual helps a close relation, such as a sibling or a cousin, to reproduce, then the altruistic act is actually helping many copies of genes that are also present in the altruistic individual's body to reproduce. Sometimes, the genes that are caused to spread in this way will include copies of the genes that made the altruistic individual act in this helpful way. And that, plus some detailed mathematical calculations by the likes of Hamilton, Trivers and Maynard Smith, is all you need to understand altruism in Darwinian terms. A gene, or set of genes, that causes individuals to behave in what we think of as an altruistic way can spread amongst the population, because its presence in some bodies (phenotypes) will lead to action which allows copies of that same gene to reproduce in other bodies! This is all best summed up by a remark that Haldane is supposed to have made in a pub in the 1950s. Discussing the puzzle of altruism over a pint or two with some colleagues, he was asked if he would lay down his life for his brother. Haldane though for a while and then replied, according to legend, 'Not for one brother. But I would for two brothers, or eight cousins.' The point is that, on average, behaviour that ensures the reproductive success of two of your full siblings, or eight of your cousins, ensures the survival of copies of every gene that you carry, simply by adding up the relatednesses. It is as good, Haldane realized, as if you lived to reproduce yourself.

Of course, Haldane's remark should not be taken too literally. People – let alone other animals – do not sit around calculating degrees of genetic relatedness before deciding whether to jump into a river to save a drowning child. But the fact that people are more likely to risk their own lives to save a close relation is so firmly established that, for example, the award of the Carnegie Medal is specifically excluded for such acts. If you want to win this bravery award, you have to save the life of someone outside your immediate family.

Once we get down to specifics like this, many people find it hard to accept that human behaviour really is dependent, in large measure, on this kind of genetic inheritance. So before we go on to look in more detail at altruism in people, it may help to see how beautifully these ideas stand up to test in other species.

THE BIRDS AND THE BEES

If you find these ideas hard to swallow at first sight, you are in good company. When Hamilton graduated from Cambridge University in

1960, and began working for his PhD at the University of London, the group selection school of thought was very much the dominant one in evolutionary debate. Hamilton found it hard to reconcile this with the precise mathematical treatment pioneered by R. A. Fisher to explain how evolution worked by selection at the individual level, and he tried to bring Fisher's ideas up to date, and make them more complete, in his PhD thesis. Unfortunately, the powers that be decided that this work was not up to the standard they required, and Hamilton was told that he could not receive a PhD for it. Nevertheless, his work was published in 1964, in a paper that Trivers has described as 'the most important advance in evolutionary theory since the work of Charles Darwin and Gregor Mendel'.[2] Even without his PhD, usually the essential meal ticket for a university scientist, Hamilton became a lecturer at University College London in 1964, and did at last receive his doctorate in 1968. Indeed, recognition came much quicker to him than to Mendel, who never lived to see the importance of his own work recognized.

Why is Hamilton's work now seen as so important? We do not want to become too deeply embroiled in the mathematics here. You can find the details, if you wish, in student texts such as the one by David Barash cited in the Bibliography. But insect communities, such as those of the bees, provide such a striking example of the success of modern ideas about gene selection that they are worth spelling out in a little detail.

Darwin himself puzzled over the behaviour of insects. In the first edition of the *Origin*, he commented on:

> one special difficulty, which at first appeared to me insuperable, and actually fatal to the whole theory. I allude to the neuters or sterile females in insect-communities; for these neuters often differ widely in instinct and in structure from both the males and fertile females, and yet, from being sterile, they cannot propagate their kind. (See pp. 203–4 of the Modern Library edition.)

Darwin follows up with his own solution to the puzzle, which is very similar to modern kin selection theory.

The problem is simple. We have what seems to be the ultimate in altruism, workers who work hard and diligently to ensure the successful

THE RULES OF THE GAME

reproduction of the queen, who produces thousands of offspring, while the workers leave no offspring behind at all. How can evolution by natural selection explain such a phenomenon? How can it possibly be 'fit' to fail to reproduce? Workers leave no offspring, so where do the workers in the next generation come from – or, in modern terms, where do the worker *genes* in the next generation come from? Stated like that, we are already on the trail of the answer. The genes come, of course, from the queen, and from the male that she mates with. But social insects are *not* among the category of creatures that reproduce in essentially the same way that people do. Males in these species (which include bees, ants and wasps) have only one set of genes, while the queen has two. And this makes all the difference.

When a queen bee produces sons, she does so without any genetic contribution from a male. Her eggs are formed by cell division so that each contains one set of genes. If the egg develops without fertilization (parthenogenetically), it becomes a male. But when she produces daughters, the eggs are fertilized in the usual way and end up with two sets of genes. Because the male – the father – has only one set of genes to copy and pass on, however, this makes the daughters much more closely related than are human siblings. The relatedness of mother and daughter is just as before, $\frac{1}{2}$. But the father now gives a copy of *all* of his genes to the daughter, so the relatedness between father and daughter is 1 – every gene in the father is copied in the daughter's genotype. All the daughters have the same father, because in such species the queen stores up the sperm provided by her partner in one mating and shares it out among her eggs as they are laid. So half the genes in all her daughters are identical, because they come from the father; and half of the other half are identical, exactly as in the case of human mothers and daughters. So the *total* relatedness between sisters in the hive is $\frac{3}{4}$ (half plus a quarter). The relatedness between sister and brother is only one-quarter, since the brother has no genes from the father and is in effect a half-sibling, while the relatedness between brothers is $\frac{1}{2}$. But it is the sisters that matter here.

As Hamilton pointed out, and calculated explicitly in his landmark contribution of 1964, the relatedness of $\frac{3}{4}$ between sisters in the hive is more than the relatedness that would exist between mother and daughter if the workers were to reproduce in the usual way. *If* a female worker were to reproduce in the way we do, she would pass on half of her genes in every new individual born. But if, instead, she helps the queen to reproduce, then on average she ensures the reproduction of three-quarters of her own genes every time a new female is born. In terms of selfish genes, it is more advantageous to give up reproduction for herself and act 'altruistically' towards her queen and sisters.

Extension of this argument explains, in detail that we shall not go into here, why there are more females than males in the hive or nest, why the males do relatively less work than the females (with a relatedness of only 0.25 it does not pay them to help their sisters), and many other features of the life of social insects. The very problem that led Darwin to wonder whether evolution by natural selection really could be applied universally became, in the hands of Hamilton, a triumphant example of evolution and selection at work at the level of genes. We have not, of course, gone into the fascinating question of how such a genetic system could have become established in the first place. As we said at the start, this book is concerned with explaining animal behaviour, and especially human behaviour, *today*, in terms of our genetic inheritance. The origin of species is outside the scope of our present discussion. What matters here is that modern Darwinism explains the continued survival of the way of life of the social insects today – a way of life that has evolved independently in twelve varieties of present-day life on Earth, including the termites, which is some measure of its success.

Bees and ants, though, are far removed from human beings, and their behaviour is far removed from human behaviour, as this modern explanation of an old problem itself shows. But some of the closest parallels with human behaviour come from species that are not the ones that most of us would immediately think of as archetypes for ourselves – birds.

The search for natural 'models' on which to base human sociobiology leads us up some strange paths. Social insects very definitely are not organized like human society, yet their peculiar genetics provide the basis for a thorough test of sociobiological ideas, tests which sociobiology passes with flying colours, Even to study one of the most characteristically human features of our social interactions we have to turn not to our closest genetic relations, the chimp and the gorilla, but to the birds. The feature of bird behaviour that is shared with the behaviour of people, but with very few other species, is that the male usually makes at least some contribution to the care of his offspring, and often plays a major role in rearing the young. This is certainly not the case in chimpanzee society, for example. Birds, like people, have what the biologists call 'a high male parental investment', and this carries with it a host of associated traits that sometimes echo our own behaviour and sometimes provide new insights into the business of being human. This is one of the principal reasons why evolutionary biologists spend so much time studying birds (the other reason is simply that there are many birds around and they are relatively easy to study). So what can the study of birds tell us about the evolution of altruism, and the reasons why it is so often, in one form or another, an ESS today?

One example may show the importance of this kind of work. Ornithologists were puzzled for many years by the observation that in many species of birds it is quite common for a young (but sexually mature) adult to make no attempt at breeding itself but to devote a great deal of energy to helping an older pair to rear their own offspring, chiefly by carrying food to the nest. This helping at the nest has now been seen in more than 140 species; it is far from being an odd freak of nature, and must represent a successful strategy, at least under certain circumstances. The puzzle is, of course, very similar to the puzzle of worker bees, since it seems that the helper is missing out on the opportunity to send copies of its own genes into the next generation, while ensuring the spread of rival genes. But there are subtle differences from the insect case, as well as similarities.

First, the similarities. As you might by now expect, in most cases the helpers are, in fact, close relations of the individuals they are helping. Very often, helpers are previous offspring of the parents, and therefore siblings to the nestlings, that they help. So there is an immediate genetic benefit, which must be offset against any reproductive cost to the helpers, in the copies of their own genes that they are aiding in the bodies of their siblings. With birds laying several eggs in one nest, it very quickly becomes possible for a variation on Haldane's quip to become a real proposition – helping three or four siblings to survive might very well outweigh the cost of not breeding yourself.

But once this pattern of behaviour becomes common, as genes for helping spread through the gene pool of the species, it can lead to more widespread effects. The pattern of behaviour that makes for helping at the nest of your siblings is almost exactly the same as the pattern of behaviour that makes for helping at the nest of any members of your species. As helping becomes a common activity, somes individual helpers, either through confusion, inability to recognize their kin, or even as the result of a very slight mutation, will help more widely. One study of Florida scrub jays, for example,[3] observed 199 helpers during an eight year period. Out of the 199, 118 were helping both their parents to raise their full siblings, 49 were helping one parent and a 'step-parent' to raise half-siblings, and the other 32 were helping various combinations of siblings, grandparents and unrelated birds. This begins to show how a characteristic that starts out on the basis of kin selection can spread through a population to become, for want of a better term, general 'niceness'. And, of course, such a tendency does now begin to act 'for the good of the species', although it has its origins firmly in the selfishness of genes.

The most important feature of all these studies is that birds with helpers do indeed rear more young from the nest than birds without helpers. But kin selection is not the whole story.

Unlike worker bees, the helpers at the nest are not sterile and could reproduce. Many of them do indeed reproduce, but only after 'learning their trade' as helpers. Some studies show that young birds who find a mate and breed as soon as they are sexually mature do not produce very many fledged offspring. Hardly surprisingly, parents with some experience of the task do a better job of rearing their young. In species where helpers do their learning at the nests of their close relations, there is no waste of effort in trying to rear offspring that fail to reach maturity, but the skills that are learned will be just as valuable in later years when the bird finds a mate and sets up a nest of its own. Indeed, observations of groups of these birds over several years show that birds that have been helpers in previous years and then become nest holders themselves do better, in the reproductive stakes, than young birds nesting for the first time without the benefit of previous experience.

And there is another parallel with human behaviour among these species. In some cases, including the Florida scrub jays already mentioned, successful helpers eventually inherit breeding space from the holders – often their own parents – when the older birds die. As we shall often see in part III, birds really do provide a useful model for some kinds of human behaviour. Altruism derived from kin selection really does have a genetic basis; while altruism of a slightly different kind may have played a big part in making us human in the first place.

THE ALTRUISTIC APE

Kin selection can explain the basis of many aspects of human altruistic behaviour. Our ancestors, in the not so distant evolutionary past, lived in small groups, a few dozen at most, where everybody was related, to some degree, to everyone else. In those circumstances, any tendency towards general altruism, provided that it did not involve too much effort or risk by the altruist, would tend to be a good thing for the genes carried by the altruist, since the survival of bodies carrying copies of those genes would be enhanced every time the altruist helped a relation. The key, of course, is the balance between cost and benefit, which has been analysed in great mathematical detail in recent years. In simple terms we would expect people to be more willing to help close kin, and not to be willing to put the same effort (or take the same risks) to help more distant relations. This is certainly true – one of the enduring features of human society is nepotism in one form or another. And a situation rather more like that of our recent ancestors occurs even now in some parts of the world.

One example the sociobiologists love to quote – quite rightly – is that of the Bering Sea Eskimos, who go hunting for whales from open boats. Whaling crews consist of individuals who are relatively close relations – brothers, fathers and sons, uncles and nephews. Whaling is a risky business, and the most successful crews will be the ones where individuals are willing to help each other even at some risk to themselves – everyone has to pull his weight, whatever the circumstances. An outsider will be less inclined to help a crew mate out of difficulties. Such examples are good circumstantial evidence in support of kin selection as a basis for altruism. But they are no more than the icing on the cake of the detailed studies of many species which show the predicted pattern of behaviour. And they do not tell the full story, since one of the key features of being human seems to have derived from another kind of altruism altogether, a seemingly cold-blooded calculation of how to maximize self-interest, which, ironically, is what goes towards making people so nice.

Wilson has described altruism as 'the mechanism by which DNA multiplies itself through a network of relatives'.[4] But Trivers has shown that this network can be extended much further, and DNA reproduction can be enhanced beyond the circle of relatives (except in the sense that all people are related to one another by common descent from some remote ancestor) by a process called reciprocal altruism. The essence of this is simplicity itself, familiar to all human beings, and can be summed up in a time-worn sentence: 'You scratch my back and I'll scratch yours.'

Reciprocal altruism provides the precise counter-example to aggression when we look at human society. Extreme aggression is fascinating because it is aberrant; reciprocal altruism is so 'obvious' to us that we take it for granted, like the little old lady who goes quietly about her daily routine without ever being mugged and appearing on TV. It requires a conscious shift of mental gears to understand why reciprocal altruism should be such an exciting topic in sociobiology. Our whole society is based upon reciprocal altruism. Economics depends upon people being willing to accept promises from each other; without trust, our financial institutions would come crashing down. Of course there are cheats – in a society of mainly altruists, it may be that cheating provides a viable way of life (an ESS) for a few. We try to minimize cheating by having rules of behaviour, carefully worded contracts, all the machinery of justice, law and order, and police. But that is only a superstructure we build on an underlying framework of innate human nature. If most of us were *not* honest reciprocal altruists, the whole system would fall apart.

Opponents of sociobiology who fear that, for example, analysis of the genetic bases of behaviour might encourage judges to give lenient sentences to, say, rapists because it is only 'human nature' have got hold of the wrong end of the stick. Our interpretation of sociobiology actually suggests that very severe sentences should be handed out for such *un*natural (as far as the majority is concerned) behaviour, thus helping to minimize deviation from the pattern of behaviour that is most appropriate for human society.

Or consider our care of the sick, something more like the image that initially springs to mind when we hear the word 'altruism'. Naive Darwinism would suggest that the sick should be left to die. Why help them to recover and breed, thereby ensuring survival of their genes, when you could grab their resources for yourself and use them to provide for your own children? Tending for the sick however, is, an important feature of human behaviour, and has been since long before the rise of our modern civilization. We pay taxes, or subscribe to insurance schemes today, partly out of our self-interest, so that when *we* are ill we can receive the necessary medical attention. But most of us have very little prospect of needing major medical attention in our youth, while we are busy raising our children. By each contributing a relatively modest amount, we ensure that the few individuals who do need this kind of help get it. The cost to the altruist – the donor – is small, but the benefit to the recipient is high, perhaps literally a matter of life and death. This is a key feature of the insight into reciprocal altruism provided by Trivers in the early 1970s.

The most readable summary of the detailed application of these ideas to many species is to be found in his book *Social Evolution*. The relevance to human beings can be stated quite briefly, starting out from one of Trivers' examples, the case of a drowning man rescued by an unrelated bystander.

This happens, of course, quite frequently in human society, sometimes at great risk to the rescuer, and occasionally with the would-be rescuer drowning as well. There is a range of human reactions to the sight of a swimmer in distress – some ignore the cries for help, many help if the situation does not look too dangerous, a few plunge in at any risk. The pattern is the same as that of all human characteristics, a spread around some typical value, just as with height, or intelligence. As ever, though, it is not the amount of variation that concerns us here as the fact that such a response, to provide help to those in need, exists, in a general way, in the human population. Why should it be 'good', in terms of the spread of his or her own genes (It is, in fact, much more likely to be a man, for reasons which will become clear in chapter 6), for the rescuer to make any effort to save the drowner at all? The crucial thing is that in most cases the drowner should have only a small chance of surviving unaided, while the rescuer has only a small chance of drowning. The cost to the altruist is small; the benefit to the recipient is great – just like medical insurance.

In modern society, of course, the two participants in the drama may never see each other again. But for millions of years of human evolution people lived in small groups, tribes and family units. In those circumstances there is a real possibility that if, one day, the former rescuer is in difficulties and needs help, then the rescued man (or woman) will remember the debt owed and will reciprocate. Now, over a period of time, *both* individuals have achieved a great benefit, each of them at little cost. In this way, any genetic predisposition to help other people out of danger will spread through the population, because altruists will be recognized by other altruists and helped in their turn, while selfish individuals who never help anyone will be less likely to receive assistance when they are in trouble.

It looks almost childishly simple when we spell it out like this, because it is so much a part of our nature. It is commonsense. But it is commonsense only because millions of years of evolution by natural selection have made it part of our nature. And it has taken a special set of circumstances acting on the members of our own species to make us the supreme reciprocal altruists among all terrestrial life forms. It does not matter that these requirements are not met by modern people living in cities today; we have only lived in cities for a tiny fraction of evolutionary time. What matters is that the conditions were met by the lifestyle of our ancestors during the past few million years, and that we carry on our cells copies of the genes that made those ancestors so successful.

The first requirement is a long lifespan, or there will be no time for reciprocation to occur. Secondly, people must live in more or less the same place for most of their lives, interacting with the same small number of people in a stable social group, where reciprocators and cheats can be identified – not necessarily consciously – and treated accordingly. And, of course, the long period of human infancy, during which the child makes contact with a wide variety of relatives over many years, helps the process along. Under those circumstances, it is natural that we should have evolved to help each other in times of danger, to share food, to help the sick, share tools, and, perhaps most important of all, to share knowledge. All of these activities involve a small cost to the donor and a great benefit to the recipient.

How would the emergence of reciprocal altruism among the groups of primitive humans described by Trivers affect their future evolution? In a burgeoning society of reciprocal altruists, laced with a few selfish cheaters, an evolutionary premium would be placed on many of the qualities that are covered by our modern term 'intelligence'. You need to recognize individuals and assess their reliability; you need some understanding of past, present and future; any move towards more efficent means of communication helps, as it becomes possible to strike genuine bargains, along the lines of 'you lend me your spear today and I'll lend you my axe tomorrow', and so on. It seems to us that, at the very least, the advantages of intelligence and speech in making us more efficient reciprocal altruists must have been a contributory factor in producing a selection pressure favouring the evolution of those human characteristics. Perhaps this was even a *key* influence in making us human. R. D. Alexander has summed up the way these pressure would encourage the development of the human brain:

> No feature of the environment is quite so difficult to figure out as what to expect from other social beings with whom we must interact, each of whom is attempting with all of the capabilities he can muster to adjust the outcome of our interactions with him to his own advantage, rather than to ours, when our interests differ. (*Darwinism and Human Affairs*, University of Washington Press, Seattle, 1979; quoted by Barash, p. 157.)

The ability to reason, and then to compromise and strike a bargain, stems naturally from the evolution of a complex society of reciprocal altruists, and has now given us the opportunity to override some of the out of date genetic programming that we still carry, as we shall see especially in chapter 8. We have become something more than instinctive automatons responding to the rules laid down in our DNA; the altruistic ape really is different from any other animal on Earth, including the pygmy chimpanzee, in a way which belies the fact that 99 per cent of our DNA is the same as theirs. But still, that altruism is itself evolutionarily advantageous; it is 'selfish' in the appropriate Darwinian sense – it is 'fit'. We can reason out why it is fit, and write books about it; we can refine our natural altruistic instincts into contracts and binding promises; we can work out for ourselves that the pattern of behaviour appropriate to a tribe of pre-Stone Age people may not be appropriate for a nation armed with nuclear weapons, without (we hope) waiting for natural selection to change our attitudes. But all of these abilities exist in people today because they are coded for, directly or indirectly, in our DNA, and because they have proved to be fit – to have survival value – in the past.

Many people – probably most people – are reluctant to accept that even acts of self-sacrifice and saintliness are part of our genetic makeup. This is interesting in itself, and some sociobiologists argue that the capacity for self-deception, to convince yourself that you are not really acting to maximize your own success, may be a trait that has been selected for together with the altruistic way of life. We must be careful not to confuse genetic selfishness with everyday selfishness – self-*sacrifice*, for an individual, may be a form of genetic selfishness if, as in the case of a bird giving a warning cry, it helps copies of certain genes in other individuals. The bird might not be willing to make the sacrifice if it knew what was going on at the genetic level! Alexander is one who points out that our biology has led to the paradox that we are genetically selfish (like all species) and also dependent on social groups for our continuing success. How can we be both selfish and social at the same time? Why should individuals, in some cases, make the ultimate sacrifice for the good of copies of their genes in the bodies of other individuals? The resolution to the dilemma may be self-deception. The best liars are said to be those who delude themselves into believing their own lies; in the same way, the best social animals – the best altruists – may be those who delude themselves into believing that they are acting solely for the good of others.

We provide crutches for our altruistic tendencies in the form of morality or religion. We tell ourselves that we should live by a moral code, or by the rules laid down by God, instructions which reinforce the relatively new evolutionary development of reciprocal altruism and help to suppress the older kind of purely selfish instincts. People are no less human, and no less altruistic, for the fact that altruism, like all other features of being human, depends on our genetic inheritance. *Everything* that we are is coded in DNA, and each of us starts out as a single fertilized cell carrying that coded DNA message. But we are not programmed like ants to act blindly in accordance with the statistical rules of relatedness. Instead, we have predispositions that incline us in certain directions. We are inclined to be intelligent, given the right environment and stimuli in infancy and childhood, and we are inclined to be altruistic – to be nice to one another, to love our neighbours. Our feelings of love, affection and friendship are no less real and no less significant for that – just as our feet, say, are no less real and no less important for the fact that their existence too depends on the message that has been passed on as strands of twisted DNA from our parents. Ethics, moral codes, and the teachings of the great religions are powerful forces in human affairs because they are right, not in any subjective sense but in the sense that the code of behaviour they represent has been tried and tested in the evolutionary struggle for survival. Peace on Earth, cooperation, helping the sick and weak and all the rest is a package that has emerged through the process of natural selection. And this makes the case for people to continue to be nice to each other, and to try even harder to be even nicer to even more people, far more compelling than if the message came from a few aberrant individuals struggling to stem the tide of rampant human aggression.

The rules of the game are clear. We are 99 per cent ape, but the one per cent advantage lies very largely in the fact that we are *altruistic* apes. We act out of self-interest, but in most cases this is enlightened self-interest. With this in mind, we can at last understand the basics of human relationships, within the family and in the wide world of politics. And *then* we shall be able to see how best to take advantage of the one per cent to make our lives better and more secure.

PART III
THE GAMES PEOPLE PLAY

6

SEX GAMES

'The meaning of sexual reproduction,' says Robert Trivers, provides 'the deepest mystery in all biology.'[1] The central feature of life, as was clear long before Darwin's day, is, of course, reproduction. Living things reproduce, making copies of themselves (not necessarily exact copies) that continue the line. To a modern biologist, this reproduction is seen in terms of copying DNA, and handing copies – possibly slightly altered copies – of genes on down the generations. But why should *two* individuals be involved in the copying process, with the result that each of them contributes only half of the DNA in the new individual? On the face of things, it would be much more efficient, in terms of copying DNA, if each individual reproduced by some sort of budding process, the way strawberry plants do when they put our runners, creating offspring, new individuals, that contain copies of *all* of the parent's DNA. So how, and why, has sex evolved? And why does it persist in the world?

The only fair answer to these questions, as Trivers's remark suggests, is, 'we don't know'. Try though they might, biologists using all the tools of the mathematical approach of the ESS, and all their latest insights into the nature of genetic material and the copying of DNA, still find it very difficult to invent kinds of biological systems in which sexual reproduction has the edge over asexual reproduction. And when they do invent such hypothetical systems, these bear little or no resemblance to the real world. The reason is simply the doubled efficiency of the asexual method in terms of copying DNA. An individual that has to mate with another individual in order to produce offspring at all suffers many disadvantages in life, seen from the evolutionary point of view, because of the need to find a mate, to go through courtship rituals, to run the risk of being surprised by a predator whilst distracted by the act of mating, and so on. But the overriding factor in all these calculations is simply that, if only half your DNA is passed on to each of your descendants, then you have to be involved in 'making' at least two descendants in order to ensure that copies of all your genes are passed on to the next generation. All the calculations show that in species as diverse as ourselves and flowers, frogs and antelope, an asexual mutant that suddenly appeared in the population – a female that gave birth to exact genetic copies of herself, without her eggs being fertilized by sperm from a male – would be so successful that her descendants would wipe out her sexually reproducing relations in a few generations of intense competition. Indeed, exactly this process has happened in some plants, such as the dandelion, which have abandoned sex and reproduce in precisely this way, sending out seeds that are fertile without ever having been fertilized. And the dandelion is a very successful plant.

Evidence such as this, together with the mathematical calculations, suggests that there may well be *no* advantage to sex, in evolutionary terms, today. Sexual reproduction may, indeed, be something that was very useful long ago, so useful that some ancestral species that practised, or invented, sex has given rise to the enormous diversity of sexually reproducing species on Earth today, although the favourable conditions have now disappeared. On that picture, sex is a hangover from an earlier era of evolution, so that sexually reproducing species are indeed at the mercy of asexual mutants. But whereas this kind of mutation can occur relatively easily in a plant (explaining the success of dandelions today), it is almost impossible for a mammal, such as ourselves, because the machinery of sexual reproduction has become so complicated. This is the basis of the claim that men are, in strict evolutionary terms, redundant today, if only women could find a way to follow the success of the dandelion in producing fertile, but unfertilized eggs.[2]

We are not particularly concerned, however, with the origins of sex in this book. Intriguing though the question is, it is one that we shall leave for the experts to puzzle over. What we *are* concerned with is the fact that people *do* reproduce sexually, with the contribution of both a man and a woman being required to produce a new human being. That basic genetic requirement is the single most important influence – together with the long infancy of the resulting baby – on human society and human behaviour. Even the most blinkered opponent of the ideas of sociobiology cannot fail to see that there are men and women in the world, and that this biological fact has social implications! Before we look at the implications, though, perhaps we ought to get the basic biology straight.

SOURCES OF SEX

Sending copies of your genes on into succeeding generations is what life, and evolution, are all about. Successful genes, ones that makes their carriers more fit, in Darwinian terms, squeeze out unsuccessful genes. In human terms, an adult female that has survived to reproductive age is obviously successful; daughters that are exact copies of herself ('clones') ought to be just as successful, so why bother mixing in a 50 per cent proportion of genes from a man? (Strictly speaking, a clone is a group of genetically identical individuals. The individuals are therefore members of the clone, in the correct, but cumbersome, terminology. In recent years, popular usage has altered the meaning of the word, so that often nowadays you see reference to 'a clone' meaning an individual that is an exact genetic copy of another individual. As good Darwinians, we follow this evolved usage of the term.)

The most obvious result of this mixing is that it produces variability. Instead of producing identical daughters (identical with each other and with herself) the mother produces children that carry new mixes of genetic material, that differ in different ways from each other and from herself and their father(s). Variability is so obviously the key feature of sexual reproduction that it must be intimately related to the origins of sex, and to the success of sex in the past. Variability can be an advantage in itself, under special conditions when the environment is changing and the mixing of genetic material involved in sexual reproduction can help advantageous mutations to spread through a population. But any advantage is usually small and only outweighs the twofold advantage of asexual reproduction under special circumstances – circumstances that probably do not apply to the vast majority of species on Earth today, and certainly do not apply to ourselves.

In everyday language, sex speeds up evolution. But that is only an advantage where there is some need for rapid evolution. That might have been true in the past, when conditions were (perhaps) more variable than they are today. Or it might be something that is true from time to time. Fossil evidence shows that there have been repeated occasions in the history of our planet when there were extinctions of many life forms. These disasters – like the 'death of the dinosaurs' some 65 million years ago – may have been linked with natural phenomena such as ice ages, or with the effects of the impacts of giant meteorites with the Earth. In the aftermath of such a disaster, sexual reproduction would be an advantage, and might have the result that species that 'use' sex become so well established that by the time things had settled down into a more stable state there would be no immediate scope for asexual mutations to take over. If a similar disaster struck tomorrow, the dandelions might well disappear, with their ecological niche being taken over, as the environment recovered, by some variation of sexually reproducing plant that survived the holocaust and spread. But then, in several million years' time, an asexual mutation might once again crop up to dominate the now-stable situation.

The best prospect of explaining why rapid evolution might be an advantage, however, comes from looking at the way predators and disease affect a population of animals.

Some of the latest ideas about the role of sex in evolution concern these links, especially those between large creatures like ourselves and the tiny organisms, bacteria and viruses, that cause disease. These micro-organisms have a very rapid life cycle, and reproduce many times in a few minutes, let alone in a human lifetime. Partly for this reason, they are constantly evolving new variations on old themes – different strains of influenza, for example, crop up every few years, and sweep around the globe. Somehow, the defences of the body have to evolve rapidly enough to counter these changes in the invading organisms, and there has to be a variety of individuals, otherwise the defences will be overwhelmed and all the identical members of the species that is being attacked – the ones that get ill – will be wiped out. It is just possible that sexual reproduction survives in the world today because it provides enough variability, and rapid enough evolution of defences against disease, to ensure that we, and species like us, are not wiped out by super bugs.

This is ironic, because we are all descended from micro-organisms very similar to the bacteria that are so potentially lethal to us today. Sex got started when pairs of those primeval bacterial-type cells 'learned' how to get together and mix their genetic material instead of just splitting into two new cells each containing an exact copy of the parent's DNA. Again, nobody can be sure exactly how such a system developed, or what the initial advantages were that gave it a leg up the evolutionary ladder. One suggestion is that by combining two copies of the primitive genetic material such early cells were able to eliminate errors – a mistake in a stretch of genetic material from one cell, which might be potentially lethal, could be rectified by taking on board a correct copy from another cell. Whatever the exact origins of the sharing process, however, it does seem that once it got started there was an inevitable tendency for a polarization which has led, down the aeons, to the two sexes, and two sexual roles, of the modern world.

The best guess we can make about the origins of sex is that it involved, for whatever reason, pairs of more or less identical cells coming together, sharing their genetic material, and then dividing into two (or more) daughter cells which each carried a different mix of genetic material from that of their parents. Such a system is sexual reproduction, all right, but it only involves one sex – all the cells are essentially the same type. It does not need the mathematical wizardry of a John Maynard Smith to see how evolutionary pressures will drive the descendants of these cells in two different directions.

There are just two ways to be successful, in terms of producing viable offspring, under such a system. It is absolutely essential to find a partner, once such a system has become established, or you will not be able to reproduce at all. And it is no less essential to provide a good store of raw material ('food'), so that each of the daughter cells is big enough to survive and function efficiently. These requirements are to a large extent opposed to one another. An active, small cell will be able to swim around rapidly in the primeval ooze and find a partner, but it will not carry much in the way of resources for the next generation. And a big, fat cell will be an excellent provider of resources but will not be very mobile and will have to wait for a 'mate' to come its way. Small cells that meet one another and mate will produce even smaller off-spring, ripe for being gobbled up by other micro-organisms; big, fat cells will not find a mate at all unless a small, mobile cell swims up to them. Immediately, we have the beginnings of the sexual system of reproduction involving two sexes – a 'female' that provides a large 'egg', and a 'male' that provides nothing more than a package of genetic material, a proto-sperm.

This is, of course, a great oversimplification of a complicated process. But it does suggest how two sexes could have emerged very early in the story of life on Earth, and it underpins the most basic feature of sex roles in human beings and many other species – the female provides a large egg, the male provides many small sperm. This does not necessarily mean that the female has to be the nurturant partner, taking care of the babies. In some species of water bug, for example, the male carries the fertilized eggs around on his back, looking after them until they hatch. Women today are committed to carrying their offspring in the womb for nine months, but many men are able and willing to take over much of the responsibility after birth. But to a biologist, the fundamental truth is that the female of any species is the one that provides the larger sex cell, or gamete – in every-day language, the egg. And the resulting differences can be crucial for the behaviour of the individual male and female members of the species, each individual being concerned with maximizing its own evolutionary success by producing as many offspring as possible.

Sex Roles and Sex Ratios

We should stress here, before we proceed further, the difference between identifying features of human behaviour and the reasons why such features have evolved, and the quite different question of whether we 'ought' to behave in a certain way. Millions of years of evolution have, clearly, produced women that are adapted to looking after babies. Leaving aside pregnancy itself, only women have breasts that produce milk for babies to feed on, and until only a few decades ago it was impossible for any man to take charge of feeding an unweaned baby. That is an evolutionary fact. But today, of course, a man can take a newborn infant and look after it entirely on his own, without any help from any woman at all, because he can obtain milk formulas derived from cows' milk to keep the baby healthy and happy. We are able to override our evolutionary inheritance through a combination of intelligence, technology, and social adaptations. But that does not mean that it is not useful to know what the underpinning biological rules of the game are.

In a similar way, our upper bodies, especially our arms and shoulders, are adapted for swinging through trees from branch to branch – a form of locomotion called brachiation. The genetic and evolutionary origins of this are clear, but that does not mean that we all use the skills of the gymnast in our daily lives. So when we discover, as we shall indeed before too long, that human evolution during the past few million years has produced males with an in-built tendency to seek more than one sexual partner, that does not mean that we are suggesting that all men 'ought' to be philanderers, any more than we say that all people ought to swing through the trees or that no man ought to feed a baby. Intelligence brings with it new understanding, new types of society (themselves biologically determined, of course, since intelligence is a biological phenomenon), and new patterns of behaviour. But if we understand the genetic imperatives that undoubtedly do incline men and women to have different attitudes towards, in this case, sex, then we shall understand better how society should take care to encourage people, where appropriate, to override those imperatives and to act in ways that are suitable for survival in the civilized world today, instead of in the African savannah three million years ago.

Reproduction is very closely related to evolutionary success, and different strategies of reproduction are particularly susceptible to natural selection. As David Barash points out,[3] the result is that 'the analysis of reproductive strategies has been one of the most productive areas of sociobiology'. We have no space to go into all the examples of this productive line of research here and shall concentrate chiefly on the examples most relevant to ourselves as human beings. It happens that we are rather unusual, as mammals go, and that our unusual features are largely a result of the long-term investment parents have to make in bringing up children – something we delve into in more detail in the next chapter. The human pattern of mating is much more like that of many birds than many mammals, and for the same basic reason – birds too have to invest a lot of effort in rearing their young to the point where they can begin to lead independent lives. Very many mammals go in for a quite different kind of mating system to the human one. Ours, of course, is dominated by partnerships between one male and one female which last for a long time. The more 'natural' system, for many mammals, involves a harem of females dominated by one or a few males – a fact which causes hackles to rise on some people, who mistakenly believe that sociobiologists who study such systems are suggesting that human males 'ought' to dominate harems of women. But this type of mating system is even more interesting because it raises a question that completely baffled Darwin himself, but which we can now answer with great ease.

Let us take the puzzle first. In a species like our own, the females are each physically capable of producing only a very limited number of offspring compared with the reproductive potential of an individual male. In fact, let us put the figures in perspective by considering the human case itself. Even allowing for the possibility of multiple births, it is extremely unlikely that any woman could produce more than 50 children that survived to reproduce in their turn. A much more realistic figure, in line with known records of women who have proved to be particularly fertile, would be half that number, say 25 children. This is simply because it takes nine months from conception to birth, during which time, of course, a further conception will not occur; indeed, it is unlikely that the woman will conceive again within three months of the birth, giving a maximum 'productivity' of one child per year. A man, on the other hand, if fit and in his prime years of sexual activity, could quite possibly mate with a different woman every day of the year, if he could find sufficient willing partners. This is, of course, extremely unlikely, but it makes our point. A man could easily become the father of as many children in the space of a couple of years as a woman can produce in her entire lifetime; and the record for male productivity (amongst the harems of old-time eastern potentates) runs into several hundred children fathered in a lifetime.

It might seem from this simple fact of life that there is no 'need' for very many males in the population. Many females are required to produce the next generation of individuals, but surely a few males would be sufficient to do the job of fathering them? In fact, this is a fallacious, group-selectionist argument. For individuals, it turns out, the best strategy, except under very special circumstances, is to become the parent of an equal number of sons and daughters.

Darwin puzzled over the phenomenon that in very many species, including our own, the ratio of males to females is very close to 1:1. He could not see why it should make any difference, in evolutionary terms, whether an individual left behind all sons, or all daughters, or some arbitrary mixture of each. The problem was solved in the 1930s, by the mathematician R. A. Fisher, simply by considering the next generation of descendants, the grandchildren of the original individuals considered.

The argument runs like this. Suppose that there is a species in which there is a genetic predisposition for females to be born, so that in the first generation of descendants from our hypothetical parents there are three times as many females as males. It immediately follows that those males will, on average, be three times more successful than the females in passing on their genes to the next generation. At one extreme, if the individuals form male–female pairs and are monogamous, two-thirds of the females will be without partners and will have no offspring; at the other extreme, if the individuals are completely promiscuous, all the females will be inseminated and will have offspring, but on average each male will have inseminated three females, so each male will pass on three times as many copies of his genes as each female to the next generation.

As long as the population is biased towards producing females, any mutation which causes one individual to produce sons instead of daughters will do well, because those sons' genes will in turn spread three times as effectively as female genes, and carry with them the mutation for maleness.

Exactly the same argument applies in reverse, if the original hypothetical population contained three times as many males as females. In that case, *females* would have greater evolutionary success, and any mutuation encouraging the production of females would spread rapidly through the population. The only stable strategy, the ESS, is when the populations of males and females are in balance, with a ratio of 1:1.

This is true even among species that practice polygamy. Again, take a hypothetical example in which there is a species where, on average, each successful male has a harem of ten females that he dominates and from which he excludes all other males. You might think, at first, that the correct strategy for a mother 'ought' to be to give birth to ten daughters for every son, since any additional sons will be wasted, in terms of evolution, and leave no descendants. But remember that each *successful* male inseminates *ten* females. He has a one in ten chance of winning a harem, and the payoff he receives is at odds of ten to one, exactly matching the chances of success. The net result is that the 'correct' ESS is still for each female to give birth to equal numbers, on average, of sons and daughters. All her daughters will reproduce, and the few sons that get any sexual success will hit the jackpot and produce ten times as many offspring as any one daughter.

The 1:1 ratio holds almost universally, not just among mammals but among all vertebrates. There are exceptions, though, and these have provided some of the neatest tests of sociobiology, confirming the accuracy of the ESS approach. Ants, for example, have the same kind of relatedness pattern that bees have, with female workers sharing $\frac{3}{4}$ of their genes with their sisters and only $\frac{1}{4}$ with their brothers. In such a situation, if you follow through the same line of argument that Fisher pioneered more than 50 years ago, it turns out that a nest in which the workers dominate the raising of the infant ants 'ought' to raise three times as many sisters as brothers, because only when the ratio of the sexes is 3:1 does the greater reproductive success of each male balance the fact that he only shares $\frac{1}{3}$ as many genes with his sisters as they do with each other. This was a classic example of a scientific prediction, made by Trivers and his colleague Hope Hare. They made the calculation first, and *then* counted the numbers of males and females in many ant colonies. Lo and behold, in all the species where this kind of relatedness holds, the 1:3 ratio does indeed occur. And that kind of successful prediction helps to give confidence in other applications of the ESS approach, and in sociobiology in general.

One of the big questions concerning human sex and reproduction is why we should, by and large, pair up with one partner for the purpose of raising children. A romantic will tell you that it is because we fall in love, and that love is forever. But, of course, love is something that has evolved, over countless generations, as a form of pair bonding. It has evolved, and persists, because it has proved to be a success in evolutionary terms – that is, people that pair up and raise children together in a stable relationship have, in the past, produced more children that live to reproduce in their turn than have people who 'chose' other forms of reproductive partnership. Any inherited tendency for people to 'fall in love' will therefore spread through the population. We can begin to see why 'falling in love' will spread through the population by looking at examples of other mammals, some of which form similar pair bonds and others of which are polygamous. Perhaps we can make our point more emphatically with an even more clear-cut example. Most people enjoy sexual intercourse, with the right partner (some do not seem to care too much about the partner). Maybe our remote ancestors did not particularly enjoy the act but carried it out instinctively, as many animals seem to do – some, including our closest relations, obviously *do* enjoy sex; others, such as honeybees and fish, seem to act purely on instinct. Once again, we see human behaviour carrying a characteristic shared with our nearest relations to an extreme. With the development of our large brains, we developed a greater capacity for pleasure, and any individuals that happened to get pleasure out of sex would be more likely than others, for obvious reasons, to leave many offspring, some of which carried that same capacity for pleasure. And, of course, any individuals that actively *dis*like sex are unlikely to leave large numbers of descendants!

WHY MONOGAMY?

The difference between the sexes is very fully expressed in mammals. Although both parents contribute their genetic material to the fertilized egg, at base level that is *all* that the male needs to contribute – a few minutes of his time, and a small amount of sperm. The female, on the other hand, is committed to weeks or months spent carrying the developing foetus inside herself, and then to a further period in which the offspring is dependent on her for milk, even if it is able, as in the case of deer, to run along with the herd almost as soon as it is born. As a general rule, females have a bigger investment in their offspring; males have little or no investment. Because females do all the work of reproduction, they are in effect a resource for which males may compete with one another. In our hypothetical example, only one in ten males get to be fathers at all, so the competition is fierce, and the rewards great – but there are natural systems, in species alive on Earth today, where competition is even fiercer.

In most species, the members of the two sexes also show marked differences in the way they choose a sexual partner. Females tend to be choosy, while males are not. Usually, each female has a choice of mates, and picks one by a process that is certainly not random (even in harems, which males win by fighting, the females are *choosing* to bestow their favours on the most successful fighting males). With most females using the same criteria for selection, this means that in many species a few males get most of the opportunities to mate. Many of the rest may miss out entirely. Among males, winner takes all, and the many losers get nothing in the reproductive stakes. So males tend to be indiscriminate in their sexual activity. It takes so little effort that by leaping at any opportunity to mate they can make sure that a few successful efforts, which result in the production of fit offspring, more than make up for the waste of time when they choose an unsuitable partner. And some choices of partner can be bizarrely unsuitable – male bullfrogs, for example, will grasp, in the mating posture, almost anything that is roughly the size of a female bullfrog, and 'almost anything' includes the foot of a wellington boot worn by someone tramping through the swamp where the frogs live! The gerbils of the Sahara Desert provide another example of the way the male takes his life in his hands to grasp any opportunity to mate, while the female is more cautious. Individual females seek out small regions, where there is a little plant life to eat, and defend them against invaders; their distribution is related to the distribution of food. But the male is driven as much by the need to mate as the need to eat. Each male will seek out a site for his burrow which is as close as possible to as many females as possible, even if that means it has little food. The distribution of males is determined by the distribution of females. Not only does he make do with a poor diet, but he risks his life repeatedly by running across hundreds of metres of open country to visit a female, on the off chance that she may be willing to mate with him before she chases him out of her precious territory. The whole business is so dangerous that the entire adult male population of an area may be replaced every few months, whereas a female has a good chance of living for a year or more, in spite of the effort she has to put into raising her young.[4]

Females are set up by their biology to be careful, literally putting all their eggs into one evolutionary basket and having a few offspring that they must raise carefully and for whom they require the fittest mate that they can obtain. Males are set up by their biology to live dangerously, to be philanderers, to mate indiscriminately and not to give a damn what happens to the offspring that they may never see, working on the basis that if there are enough of those offspring some are bound to survive. The rule holds throughout the animal kingdom, so why should people be different, if indeed we *are* different?

European red deer, which have been studied in great detail by Cambridge University researcher Tim Clutton-Brock and his colleagues, provide an archetypal example of the mammalian mating strategy, and how it is different for males and females. The male deer – stags – are bigger than the female deer – hinds – and have impressive antlers, which they use in fights with other males. The biggest stags, with the most impressive antlers, generally win those fights, which is why the species has evolved in this direction. A successful male may hold a harem of as many as 20 hinds from which he excludes all other males, so that he is the father of all the offspring born to those hinds. He achieves a very high reproductive success in the short term, directly as a result of his size, his antlers and his competitiveness, fathering 20 or more offspring in the course of two or three years. However, he is soon exhausted by his efforts to maintain his harem and to exclude other stags, and will be defeated, sooner rather than later, by a younger, fitter stag that takes over the harem. And while a few stags father more than a score of offspring each, most stags leave no offspring behind at all.

The situation for the hinds is quite different. Virtually every female that lives to breeding age will indeed breed, but, of course, each one can only produce one offspring in a season. Even the most successful hind will produce only a dozen or so offspring in her lifetime, perhaps half as many as the most successful stag. But she will not be involved in the stress of fighting, and she will almost certainly live longer than the successful male. And these lifestyles are implicit in the mammalian method of reproduction, as we have seen. Males 'should' be inclined towards polygyny, because they have much to gain by this system of reproduction if they are successful. To the female, it makes little or no difference whether she is polygamous as long as the father of her offspring is an evolutionarily fit male. (It is, of course, an advantage for a female if the father of her offspring is a big, successful male, since it is likely that he will pass on these attributes to her sons, who will grow up to be big successful males and father many offspring in their turn, carrying copies of her own genes on with theirs into succeeding generations. So it is no mystery that evolution should have selected females that 'choose' to stay in the harems.)

This last point is strikingly borne out by the behaviour sometimes observed in lion prides. These groups are built around a core of breeding females, with two or three adult males and the young of the pride. Young males are thrown out of the pride before they become sexually mature, so the dominant males father all of the offspring – until they are ousted in their turn by outsiders, perhaps youngsters ejected by another pride, as the dominant males become older and weaker. When that happens, the 'new' males immediately kill all the cubs in the pride and begin an almost frantic round of mating with the females. From the males' 'point of view', this is logical. The cubs they have inherited are no kin of theirs, and do not carry their genes. In terms of survival of their own genes, the right thing to do is to get rid of these unwelcome nuisances and get the females pregnant with their own offspring. Removing the cubs has a twofold advantage – it destroys the offspring of what are rival lines, in terms of evolution, and it also causes the females to come into oestrus. But why should the females 'allow' such behaviour? Surely it is in their interest to see their own cubs survive?

This obvious truth is only half the story. The females 'want' their cubs to survive, but it does not really matter who the father of those cubs is, provided he has proved his fitness. Presented with a *fait accompli* – dead cubs – the best strategy for the female is to mate with the dominant male(s) as soon as possible and produce new cubs that will be raised to maturity by the pride. And, of course (although perhaps at rather too subtle a level to have much effect on the evolution of this system), the 'new' father must be 'fitter', in some sense, than the old one, since he has just won a takeover battle with the previous dominant males. We do not wish to labour the point, but a little thought along the lines indicated by the lions' example provides very interesting insights into the stories of wicked stepfathers and wicked stepmothers that are immortalized in so many legends and fairy stories such as *Cinderella* and which clearly echo some deep human experience.

It is so easy, indeed, to see why polygamy, and especially polygyny (in which one male mates with several females), is the right evolutionary strategy for mammals that biologists are much more interested in the exceptional cases where mammals are monogamous, especially in view of the bearing that insight into those special cases has on our own way of life.

One very neat approach to this problem has been made by biologists such as Burney Le Boeuf, of the University of California, Santa Cruz, who have studied closely related species with similar lifestyles but different mating systems. Le Boeuf has paid particular attention to the elephant seals, in which dominant males control enormous harems and father very many offspring, and other pinnipeds, such as crabeater seals and harp seals, that are monogamous. Elephant seals are, in any case, interesting as an example of an *extremely* polygynous species. The males, up to 4 m long and weighing 3 000 kg, are as much as five times larger than the females, and this is interpreted as a direct result of the fierce competition between males in their efforts to become owners of harems. Throughout the animal kingdom, this kind of difference in size between the sexes – sexual dimorphism – is associated with polygyny, and it is a reliable rule of thumb that the greater the difference in size between males and females the bigger the size of the harem that a successful male will dominate (and, of course, the greater the number of males that never get to breed at all). The higher the reproductive stakes, the bigger the male of the species. Elephant seals mate on land on the beaches of islands off the coast of California and Mexico, where hundreds of females lie packed in side by side, like sardines in a tin, and males are involved in prolonged, bloody battles which end with a few of them gaining the 'right' to mate with an enormous harem.

There are 34 members of the Pinniped order, to which elephant seals belong, and 21 of them breed on land, in similarly restricted sites, crowded onto beaches or narrow sandbars. All but three of these are highly polygynous. Although less is known about the 13 species that breed on ice, most of them are clearly monogamous, and during the breeding season they are seen in isolated pairs, or in 'triads', a mother, her year old offspring, and her mate. Where the females are crowded together, the archetypal male strategy of polygyny is allowed to evolve to extremes. But on the ice, females do not crowd together – sharks, killer whales or polar bears all prey on pinnipeds, and a crowd of seals huddled on the ice would be extremely vulnerable to predators, Probably, indeed, it was the predators that drove the ancestors of the elephant seals and other shore breeders out of the sea to give birth. This in turn led to crowding on the few available islands, and the rise and rise of polygyny. Ice breeders followed a different tack. First, there is much more ice than there is safe beach, so there is room for females to spread out, each well able to obtain food from the sea nearby. In addition, the ice breaks up as spring progresses, so there is a limited time during which it is safe to give birth, and almost all the females do indeed give birth at the same time – which means they must all have mated at the same time. A spread-out population of females, each member of which needs to find a mate at the same time each season, inevitably implies that there is one male mating with each female.

Exceptions to these simple rules, such as species that breed on ice held fast to the coast of a landmass, also have breeding strategies that are explained by the special requirements of their environments. The details need not concern us. What we are interested in establishing here is that although polygamy, and especially polygyny, is the basic reproductive strategy of mammals, there are special circumstances in which this basic strategy has been altered by the environment to produce other breeding systems, including fairly strict monogamy. When a sociobiologist says that polygamy is the natural strategy for mammals, that is *not* the same as saying that polygamy is the natural strategy for people. True, we are mammals. But, like the crabeater seals, we are a special case. We are *almost* monogamous; however, it does seem that we still carry traces of a polygynous past, part of our basic mammalian inheritance.

Monogamy is more common in birds than in any other group of animals, and is the rule in more than 95 per cent of all known bird species. As we have seen, this is related to the enormous effort that parents have to make to raise their chicks successfully, an effort that requires the full time attention of both parents. Although there are species in which various forms of polygamy operate, and there are species in which males try to take advantage of opportunities to mate with females while the female's partner is otherwise occupied, by and large monogamy literally rules the roost. This is reflected in the similarity between the two sexes in such species – a male swan, for example, differs little in size or even plumage from a female swan, and even in species where the male goes in for gaudy plumage in order to attract a mate there is little difference in body size between males and females because the males do not physically fight one another for control of a harem.

Starting from a typical mammalian mode of reproduction, human beings have gone a long way down the same path as that taken by birds, and for the same reason – the need for both parents to cooperate in raising the young, if the young are to survive to maturity and reproduce in their turn. But we have not yet gone as far down that path as the vast majority of bird species.

Unlike so many bird species, the human species *is* characterized by a sexual dimorphism in body size. On average, men are about eight per cent bigger than women. In any other species this would immediately suggest to a biologist studying the species that there is competition between males for females, and that the most successful males 'ought' to have two or three wives while many have only one wife and a significant number fail to find a mate at all. This clearly is not true of modern western society, where monogamy is the rule – or, at least, where one man and one woman are partners for a time, even if the partnership is broken up by divorce and both partners then form new monogamous relationships (and it is no coincidence, of course, that divorce most commonly occurs after the children of a marriage are big enough to stand on their own feet). So is the theory that sexual dimorphism is related to polygyny wrong? Probably not.

What the difference in size between men and women really tells us is that there has been a selection pressure favouring slight polygyny *at least until very recently* during human evolution. Even if conditions in the civilized world today do not favour polygyny, we still carry the genes for males to be bigger than females, and to compete with one another. It will take many generations for the tendency towards sexual dimorphism to be diluted and washed away. Of course, it is easy to see how in primitive society these differences could have arisen – two women at home looking after the children, with one man to be the father of those children and keeping off potential rivals, makes a family unit that is recognizably one with survival value when it comes to rearing human infants. We are not suggesting, however, that the poor, helpless women needed the man to protect them and to provide food by hunting, although we do, of course, accept (one of us reluctantly) that a woman in late stages of pregnancy would indeed need help from other human beings in order to find food and survive. The fact that this other human being might very well be another woman, however, probably tells us more about the basic unit of two women and one man than does the myth of man the great protector. Two or three women in a family group could feed themselves and their growing children, tolerating the existence of a man that they need to father the infants but who they throw out, as often as they can, to amuse himself with hunting or with fighting other men. Most studies of 'primitive' societies show that women provide most of the food, by gathering, and that men are only able to contribute a little by hunting. In our hypothetical family group, the women 'need' the man primarily as a father for their children, and secondarily to provide some assistance with obtaining food.

As society has developed, two new evolutionary pressures worked against this family unit. First, one man and one woman – or, perhaps we should say, one woman on her own – have become well able to raise several children together, thanks to inventions such as agriculture and technology. Secondly, society as a whole is now able to take all or part of the burden of child rearing, through creches, nursery schools, and schools proper, releasing woman almost entirely from what has been their primary biological function since the mammal line began. Some of these changes occurred thousands of years ago, others only within the past few centuries and decades – a mere eyeblink in evolutionary time. Small wonder, then, that even the most civilized of us still carry genes that were selected for under quite different conditions from those we live in – and small wonder that many societies in the world today still conform more closely to the mammal stereotype than those of us who live in cities such as London and New York might appreciate.

Researchers Martin Daly and Margo Wilson, in their book *Sex, Evolution and Behavior*, list several examples that bear this out. In general terms, among all human societies investigated, polygynous marriage is common, while polyandry (one woman taking several husbands) is rare. Out of 849 societies investigated, they say, polygyny occurs in 708. It is common in roughly half that total, and occasional in the other half. Monogomy is the common pattern in just 137 societies, and polyandry is found in just four, all of them special cases where biologists can see reasons for the system being practised.

The same kind of studies highlight other features of human relationships. Whereas in most mammal species sexual relations are largely impersonal, and alliances between males and females are at best temporary, there is no human society in which sexual relations are casual and impersonal. Marriage of some kind occurs universally, in all cultures, but, as we would expect of mammals that are being pushed into monogamy, bachelors are more likely to be found than spinsters. Although a majority of *societies* allow polygyny, the majority of *marriages* are monogamous, because even in societies where polygyny occurs it is only the most powerful, or wealthy, men that take more than one wife at a time. And when it comes to choosing a mate, both men and women are as predictable in their behaviour as the males and females of other species.

CHOOSING A MATE

The way in which marriage is institutionalized by society shows how intelligently our ancestors coped with the sociobiological implications of our genetic inheritance, long before the concepts of genes and sociobiology were invented. As a social way of life emerged, it must have been clear to the intelligent leaders of tribes, or villages, or whatever units of society they were, that young, unattached males are troublemakers. They fight amongst themselves, chase after the girls, and generally carry on in a disruptive manner. But, by and large, males that have settled down with a mate are good, hardworking members of society. With the sexes roughly in balance numerically, the best way to settle everyone down is to marry off each young male with one female, maximizing the calming influence of matrimony. This is a good thing for society but runs counter to our genetic inheritance – and that is why marriage is built around with rules and customs and became a great institution. If it were as natural for human beings to pair off for life as it is for swans, then there would be no need for the institution of marriage at all. This is just the kind of insight sociobiology can provide, and, hopefully, further sociobiological insights will help us to tailor our institutions even more accurately to the needs of society, and of individuals within society, in future.

One rather good example of this is provided by the attitude of society towards incest, which represents a rather unusual form of choosing a mate, but which holds enough fascination for many people to show that it has a special place in the evolutionary story. There are good biological reasons why individuals should prefer, by and large, not to mate with their brothers or sisters, and mechanisms to avoid such incestuous relationships have evolved in most vertebrate species. The reasons why brother–sister matings are often bad, in terms of evolution, is that if the brother and sister both carry copies of a defective gene then there is an increased risk that their children will inherit that allele on both the relevant chromosomes, so that the child will not develop properly and may be deformed, or sickly, or die young. As a result, natural selection will favour individuals that choose, for whatever reason, not to mate with their siblings. Such outbreeding individuals will, by and large, tend to have healthier and, in the Darwinian sense, fitter offspring.

The evolutionary mechanisms that avoid incest have evolved many times and operate in different ways – the way lions expel male cubs from the pride before they reach sexual maturity is one obvious example, which we particularly like because it shows that a social mechanism may be selected for by more than one evolutionary pressure. The dominant males expel potential rivals *and* remove the risk of incest, killing two evolutionary birds with one stone. We do not say that the ancestors of today's dominant males started to expel youngsters in order to avoid incest; but once this behaviour is established as a successful evolutionary strategy, it will be reinforced because it promotes outbreeding – as long, of course, as outbreeding is a 'good thing' in its own right.

In other species, such as mice and rats, individuals are reluctant to mate with their littermates, who they may well be able to identify by smell. It is literally true, in many species where several young are reared together, that familiarity breeds contempt, in sexual terms, and our own species also seems to operate like this.

Children that are reared together and play together in unrestrained fashion almost never become marriage partners in later life. This is shown most clearly by the example of the Israeli kibbutz system, where youngsters from different biological parents have been reared together as if they were members of one big family. In spite of the often deep wishes of the parents of young men and women from the same kibbutz to marry each other, there is no recorded case of this ever happening. The human incest avoidance system, whatever it may be, operates on the basis that the children you are brought up with should not be sexually attractive to you in adult life – rather than, say, by sense of smell.

This is especially interesting, of course, because in prudish 'Victorian' societies boys and girls are kept apart and not allowed to play together even within the same biological family. And this can have exactly the opposite of the intended effect, since in adult life the young man and woman, although biologically siblings, have never received the 'message' that they should not regard each other as potential mates!

But there is even more relevance in all this to society today. Thanks to modern contraceptive methods, there is no reason why a brother and sister should not, if they wish, choose to be sexual partners. And thanks to modern techniques in genetic counselling and genetic engineering, there is no longer even any evolutionary reason why they should not have normal, healthy children. The incest 'taboo' has arisen in society in the first place because the way in which children were being reared had removed, at least partially, nature's instinctive incest avoidance mechanism; but the taboo is no longer necessary at all, because of further changes in society. Here is a clear-cut case where sociobiological insight can help us to change the rules of society – as has been done in Sweden, for example – to allow for increased happiness, and much less misery, for some members of society.

Apart from avoiding your immediate kin, however, the human preference when seeking a mate seems to be to grab the nearest one that is free. This rather mundane conclusion is the result of a wealth of research carried out by David Buss, of Harvard University. People tend to find marriage partners among the people they see most often, their neighbours at home, at work or at college. One of the slightly less obvious conclusions that Buss's work has shown, however, is that there is no truth in the old saying that 'opposites attract'. In fact, people tend to marry people who are as much like themselves as possible, in intelligence, social class, and even appearance – a tendency sufficiently pronounced that some researchers use the term 'associative narcissism' to describe it. There are, though, some differences between what women and men look for in a mate. When surveyed, women consistently indicate a greater preference than men for a partner who has good earning capacity, comes from a good family background, has professional status and is kind and gentle. The attributes in a life partner that men value more highly than women include physical attractiveness, frugality, and being a good housekeeper. These require-ments conform so clearly to the differences between male and female mammalian reproductive strategies that there is no need for us to highlight them further, except in one regard.

In terms of evolutionary success, the prime requirement that a man should seek in a marriage partner is a combination of youth and health. A young, healthy woman will be able to produce many children for him, so over countless generations men who prefer to mate with young, healthy women left more descendants than men who preferred older women. In that sense, it is natural that men today, descended from many generations of such matings, should be most strongly attracted to young women, just past puberty. A women, on the other hand, required rather different attributes in a partner, until very recently. She needed a male that had proved himself fit, like the red deer stags. And the way a man proves himself fit is, firstly, by surviving to a reasonable age and, secondly, by achieving wealth or status within society. A woman who mated with a successful older man was likely to leave more descendants, in the long run, than a woman who chose a young, unproven male as her partner.

Although the reasons why partnerships between older men and

younger women should have proved evolutionary successes in the past no longer apply in the same way in modern society, this insight enables us to understand why it is still true that older men are attracted by younger women and vice versa. Of course, there are exceptions – as in all our examples, we are talking only about statistical rules, which apply by and large throughout the community. Some young men prefer older women as sexual partners, but they are a minority and do not weaken the main thrust of the argument.

This particular insight can again tell us something useful about things we are doing wrong in society today. Advertisers who use very young, pre-pubescent girls dressed up in adult clothes and makeup to promote their products have recently come under attack from pressure groups who suggest that this kind of advertising encourages some men to treat children as sex objects, and may be directly linked to a rise in the number of cases of sexual abuse of children. The insight provided by sociobiology strongly supports this contention. Powerful forces have moulded human males over a long time so that their sexual urge should be directed at young women. It is no surprise that by presenting girls that have not yet reached puberty in a 'disguise' which makes them look more mature it is possible to cause this natural mechanism to overreact, with disastrous consequences for some individuals. But the advertising would not produce this reaction – indeed, it would not exist – if men were not selected to find young women particularly attractive.

Once again, the majority of men will not be affected in this way – certainly not enough to lead to attacks on young girls. But just as a few men are attracted to older women, so a few may already find extremely young women, or girls, more attractive than others. Society should take great care not to confuse such individuals further, and in sociobiological terms we regard the case against this kind of advertising as proven.

The phenomenon of like attracting like, however, also sheds new insights on the recent evolution of *Homo sapiens*. This process – called 'assortative mating' in the jargon – tends to increase the frequency of the occurrence of combinations of genes (genotypes) that produce extreme phenotypes. At the same time, it decreases the frequency of genotypes that produce more average phenotypes. Take height as an example. Tall men and tall women tend to marry one another, more often than not. Short people also tend to pair up. So short people have short offspring, while tall people rear tall children, whereas if each tall man married a short woman, and vice versa, there would be a tendency in the next generation for height to even up.

Small effects like this can produce significant changes over many generations, increasing the differences between people. And since people today are more mobile than ever before, meeting many more other people in their lives than our ancestors did, there is more opportunity than ever before for individuals to pair up with other individuals that are very similar to themselves. Increasing mobility may be decreasing, not increasing, the variability of individuals within the human population!

Men, Women and the Future

Sociobiology and evolutionary theory tell us that there are real differences between men and women, apart from the obvious physical ones. These differences may or may not be advantageous today in evolutionary terms, but we have inherited them because they gave a selective advantage to our ancestors. Women are indeed more nurturant than men, more protective, and less inclined to take risks. Men are more inclined to take risks, to show off and to be competitive. Men *are* more likely to be sexually promiscuous than women, and to be less forgiving than women if their partners indulge in sexual liaisons outside the pair. Some of the greatest achievements in human literatures, and more than a few popular songs, are built around these themes. This is an inevitable consequence of our mammalian system of reproduction – a man who strays outside the matrimonial bed but returns home may continue to be a good provider and effective assistant in raising a family; but a woman who 'strays' in this way may produce a child which is no relation to her partner but which he wastes time and effort helping to rear, at the cost of an opportunity to pass on his own genes. If a woman could get away with it, though, there might well be some evolutionary advantage to her line if she found a way to mate with a powerful, successful male whose resulting progeny was then reared by her unsuspecting, lower status husband as if it were his own. We stress that we are not suggesting that it is morally correct for people to behave like this today, or that such behaviour has any evolutionary advantage now. But because such activity did have advantages for our ancestors, it is inevitable that we carry genetic predispositions in certain directions, just as lions are genetically predisposed to kill cubs when they take over a pride. After all, 99 per cent of our genes are animal genes.

Society has developed rules, and institutions like marriage, in order to help people to overcome these genetic predispositions, and to act in ways which are more appropriate today, but for which we have not yet had time to evolve the appropriate genetic predisposition. Sociobiology can, surely, make the task of living by these rules easier, by helping us to understand both why the rules are important and why people sometimes have urges to break them.

The basic high risk/high stakes approach of the male also explains masculine behaviour in other areas of life. Throughout their lifespan men have a higher mortality rate than women of the same age, a reflection of the greater stakes that our male ancestors have played for in the reproductive game in the past. This is a direct result of the effect of testosterone on the male body, making men more aggressive and more willing to take risks. The evidence shows clearly from studies of castrated males. 'Intact' men seem to live life at a more hectic pace, so their bodies burn out more quickly – the average lifespan of a group of castrated males in American homes for the mentally retarded is 69.3 years, compared with 55.7 years for a carefully chosen sample of equivalent 'intact' men in the world outside. And, indeed, the reason why castration was practised for a time in American institutions of this kind was precisely because it made the inmates more docile and manageable.[5] You can see the same effect at work in your domestic cat. The intact tom cat leads a far more exciting and adventurous life than his castrated littermate, who sleeps slothfully by the fire. But the neutered cat lives a longer life. Testosterone is the immediate cause of typically male behaviour, but, of course, the human body has evolved to respond in this way to testosterone because typically male behaviour has been successful, in terms of passing on genes to succeeding generations. The shorter lifespan has been outweighed by the increased opportunities to reproduce.

Men are more likely than women to be killed in accidents – car accidents, mountain climbing, hang gliding or whatever – but they are also more prone to disease. The reason is easy to see, with hindsight. In primitive society a pregnant woman who gets sick is likely to lose the baby she is carrying, which represents a great loss of her reproductive potential, even if she soon recovers. A man who gets sick may feel dreadful for a while, but gets off his sickbed and impregnates another female the next week. And, of course, there is the very different implication for a young infant's prospects of survival if its mother dies, cutting off its food supply, or if its father dies. There has been a strong selection pressure for women to be fit and healthy, but far less selection on men to be fit and healthy – and, in evolution, things that are not selected for do not, by and large, evolve.

Extreme versions of male and female patterns of sexual behaviour are found among homosexuals. Homosexual men tend to be promiscuous and have many partners; homosexual women tend to have few partners or one partner in a long-term relationship. The origins of homosexual behaviour are far from clear, and provide a debating ground for experts with whom we would not wish to cross swords ourselves. But there does seem little doubt that these attitudes towards sex do represent, in some sense, the extreme sexual strategies of males and females, unfettered by the need for compromise implicit in a heterosexual relationship.

So what should we do about the differences between the sexes? We are not saying that they are 'right' today, only that they were the successful strategies selected by evolutionary pressures acting on our ancestors. In modern society, relationships between men and women (or between members of the same sex) can take very many forms and still healthy children are brought into the world and grow up to have children in their turn. We learn from sociobiology that men and women are born with different innate abilities, inclined in slightly different directions which roughly correspond with the stereotypical roles of male and female. Society, even today, acts to emphasize those differences, to make men more masculine and women more feminine. But those roles are no longer essential, nor necessarily appropriate, in society. A woman can head a corporation, or fly an airliner (but how many do?); a man can be a househusband, or in charge of a creche (but how many are?).

The key to a happier society, for both men and women, lies in the strength (or, rather, weakness) of the genetic predisposition towards male or female roles. In fact, the predisposition is small, as has been shown by studies of boys reared as girls after unpleasant accidents during circumcision, and of genetically female girls who have been subjected, for various reasons, to the influence of male hormone early in their lives as foetuses. The differences between the sexes are real, but small. As sociobiologist Edward O. Wilson has put it, 'at birth the twig is already bent *a little bit*'[6] (our italics). But there are enormous differences in the exact roles of the sexes in different human societies, and the success of the cultural influences in 'training' those boys to be 'feminine' shows that, as always seems to be the case, both nature *and* nurture are responsible for the adult. The sexual division of labour, says Wilson, 'is not entirely an accident of cultural evolution'.[6] But there is a clear implication that cultural influences can work with or against the slight biological inclination of a developing human being towards masculinity or feminity.

Our society has been, and still is, dominated by men, and has also acted to exaggerate sexual differences in behaviour. Even women, such as Margaret Thatcher, who have made it to the top of our society have done so by being, apparently, more masculine than the men, almost caricaturing the supposed male attributes – the 'Iron Lady' was described at the time of the Falklands War as being 'the only real man' in the government. We believe that the lesson to be drawn from a sociobiological perspective on the origins of sex roles is that society can and should take positive steps to reduce the natural differences. Culture can go a long way towards creating a more equal society, but this will not be achieved simply by passing laws which say that men and women are equal. It has to start at the beginning, with education. Boys should be actively encouraged to develop traditionally feminine interests and skills; girls should be encouraged to take up things traditionally associated with boys. Only then will we be using our one per cent advantage over the apes to effectively circumvent our animal genes. But we shall have to use that one per cent to its utmost if we are ever to work out exactly how this should be achieved. For example, many proponents of sexual equality fought long and hard, in many countries, to ensure that boys and girls are taught together in the same classrooms. We believe – one of us on the basis of direct experience as a school teacher – that they should be taught separately, in single-sex schools, for two reasons. First, boys and girls develop, physically and mentally, at different rates; it is ludicrous to teach mixed sex classes of children, grouped on the basis of age alone, between the ages of about 10 and 18. Secondly, largely because of the culture we are at present stuck with, girls tend to defer to boys even at an early age, and several studies have shown that girls in single-sex schools do *better* (given appropriate opportunities) in traditionally male areas such as science than do girls in mixed schools, where the boys dominate such activities.

Shaw's Professor Higgins asked, 'why can't a woman be more like a man?' Our answer is that she can, and so can a man be more like a woman. The world would certainly be a happier place if both sexes could be brought up to accept a more equal middle role; but it is very hard to see how such a desirable state of affairs can be achieved, starting from our present position.

7

THE GENERATION GAME

Why is the helpless, dumb blond, as portrayed so memorably by
Marilyn Monroe, a successful role for some individual members of
human society? The reasons lie in our genes as much as in our culture,
and have to do with the size of our brains and the resulting helplessness
of human babies.

Human babies are physically helpless. They survive only because
their helpless appearance promotes a strong response among most
adults. Even male chauvinists who profess a profound dislike of infants
will coo over a newborn baby, responding to some deep-seated
biological imperative, while a mother is able to identify the whimper
of her own baby in a busy maternity ward, and when at home will
wake at the first cry in the night, even if she was previously a heavy
sleeper. It is easy to see how such responses must have evolved in
tandem with the helplessness of the human baby at birth – a helplessness which is itself, remember, directly related to the evolution of
the large brain that makes us so successful as adults. In primitive
societies, human beings that are repelled by helpless infants do not, for
obvious reasons, leave many offspring to carry their genes forward
into future generations. Some men may, but scarcely any women
before the development of a civilized society in which it is possible for
child rearing to be taken over almost at birth by people who are not
the biological parents of the infant. So parents who respond more
lovingly to the helpless appearance of their own babies will be more
effective at raising children and ensuring the spread of their own
genes, including the package of interacting genes that makes them

love babies. And this raises the possibility of an interesting evolutionary feedback.

THE SUCCESSFUL SMILE

The kind of feedback can best be understood by considering the peacock's tail. This is a wonderful accoutrement, which is used by the male bird solely as a lure to attract females and to obtain a mate. The female birds are, obviously, attracted by the tail. We do not have to know why this should be so in order to understand the feedback process – which is just as well, since some of the arguments put forward to 'explain' the phenomenon are quite tortuous. Some people have suggested that the appearance of the tail, with the colours of the feathers making a pattern of a myriad eyes, may hypnotize the hen bird into submission; others argue that, since such a large tail is a physical handicap to the peacock, only an otherwise very 'fit' bird could survive while carrying such a handicap, and so females have been selected to mate with the males with the biggest tails. Whatever the reason, though, in the world today peahens *do* prefer to mate with peacocks with large, colourful tails. Because the peahens are, in human terms, obsessed by this characteristic, any male with a bigger tail will mate successfully and have many offspring. So genes that provide for large, colourful tails spread rapidly through the population, and the present extravagant display can evolve from a much smaller feature over many generations.

Now let us get back to parents and babies. Successful parents are those that respond to the helplessness of their babies with love and attention. So packages of genes that promote this parenting response are widespread in human populations – almost universal. In such a situation, it may actually be in the best interests of the baby to seem to be even more helpless than it really is, because that will promote a stronger parenting response. The baby, in other words, may actually be manipulating its parents, psychologically, from the moment it is born. It has to. As Robert Trivers has pointed out, because the infant is much smaller and weaker than its mother, it cannot physically fling her to the ground and suckle when it is hungry, so psychological weapons are the ones it must use to achieve its objectives.

Of course, even newborn babies are not completely helpless. They can suck, cry, see, hear and grasp. They really do look even more helpless than they are. But the relationship is not all one way. Evolution has provided the baby with a powerful means of rewarding its parents for all the attention it gets – the smile. Crying communicates a baby's distress, and this essential means to stimulate adults into action is present at birth. Within a very few weeks, however, the baby also develops a smile, so heat-warming that many other adults (especially women) apart from its parents respond to it. The smile encourages adults to interact with the baby, play with it, goo over it, and tickle its toes. It also makes the adult feel good; it is a reward to the adult for bothering to pay attention to the infant. And, once again, it is easy to see how such a system has evolved through a feedback process like the one which has made the peacock's tall so big. There is no conscious thought involved, any more that a peacock thinks 'Hm, I'd like to grow a big tail.' It is all instinctive – that is, it is coded in our genes. Once babies started to smile, back in evolutionary history (and it may have been simply a grimace connected with wind pain to start with), then adults who responded to the smile were favoured by selection, because they gave their babies more attention and helped them to grow up successfully. So infants that smiled more were favoured more, and so adults who responded were further favoured, generally speaking, and so on. The result is that we all carry genes which ensure that we smile a lot as babies (whatever culture may do to change that pattern of behaviour as we get older), and we all carry genes that make us respond warmly to smiling people, especially helpless, smiling infants.

Which brings us back to Marilyn Monroe. Just as infants are physically weaker than their parents, so women are, by and large, physically weaker than men. Abhorrent though the image may be to many women today, the stereotype of a big, husky male and a weaker female is unfortunately close to the truth, and just as babies use psychological weapons to get their way with adults, so women can, consciously or unconsciously, use psychological weapons rather than brute force to get their way with men. And what better weapon to use than the one which has proved such a success with the babies – an appearance of helplessness, combined with a fetching smile? The success of the not-so-dumb blond in melting the heart of a husky he-man is no surprise at all to the sociobiologist, but simply reflects a distortion for adult use of the infant's prime weapons in the generation game.

FORMING THE BOND

If anyone doubted the essential need for a newborn baby to latch onto the set of instinctive responses that makes its mother love it, a study carried out by two doctors in Cleveland in the early 1980s underlines the power of the mechanism. Marshall Klaus and John Kennell started out from the initially baffling puzzle that although improved medical care was enabling doctors to save many premature babies that would have died even a few years before, proportionately far more of these infants than full-term, normal infants later came back to their hospitals as victims of baby battering or neglect. It was as if the long seperation of the baby from its mother, while it was in intensive care in an incubator, had meant that the normal instinctive bond between mother and child had failed to form at birth, and that by the time the babies were returned to their mothers it was too late for the bond to form.

Again, we do not need to go into the means by which the bond-forming process is triggered – perhaps it is related to hormones that are present in the mother's body at birth but not a few days, or weeks, later. But one interesting feature noted by the Cleveland team[1] is that new born babies are remarkably alert for the first 40 minutes or so after birth. Their eyes are wide open, bright, and move to follow a moving object, especially a human face. A mother holding her newborn infant almost always concentrates on its eyes, and is often heard talking to it, saying something like 'Just open your eyes so I'll know you're alive', even though the baby is quite obviously alive and kicking! The mother automatically aligns the baby so that she can look into its eyes, and the bonding process seems to involve eye contact between mother and baby immediately after birth – almost literally, love at first sight.

So Klaus and Kennell have pioneererd a more 'natural' approach to mother–baby relationships within the hospitals where they work, an approach which is now gaining much wider acceptance. There are still problems with tiny, premature babies that must be kept in incubators if they are to survive at all. But some mothers are now able, and encouraged, to spend time alone with their baby immediately after birth, and to spend much longer with the newborn infant every day than has been the norm in hospitals. The first infants to benefit from this approach are now reaching school age, and they seem to show the benefits of a close mother–child bond. Continued monitoring of their progress over the past few years has shown that the so-called 'early contact' mothers have been more attentive to their children, with one result that the children have richer vocabularies, are more confident, and have been stimulated to the point of having measurably higher IQs than their peers – a complete vindication, incidentally, of Binet's original ideas about intelligence. And, indeed, the incidence of baby battering among this group is zero.

These are all, clearly, good things from the point of view of the adult as well as the child. But some of the most interesting evolutionary insights into the relationship between parents and children come from studies of areas of conflict – where the needs of the child and the needs of the adult are *not* the same. It might seem that what is good for the child must be good for its parents, who want to ensure that it survives to carry their genes on into the future. But this misses the point that parents are also able to 'invest' in other children. To the parent, one child is as good as another as a gene carrier; but each child, sharing only half its genes with a sibling (or indeed with a parent) 'cares' much more for its own good than for theirs, in evolutionary terms. And that is where things get interesting.

The Battle of the Generations

This is still a new and developing area of scientific research, and the detailed implications, especially for human beings, are very far from being fully worked out. But that does not make the broad outlines of the work in progress any less fascinating.

It all began in 1974, when Trivers published a scientific paper on parent–offspring conflict. He has since developed the theme more fully, but the best succinct statement of what the idea is all about is in Martin Daly and Margo Wilson's *Sex, Evolution and Behavior*. The important point is the degree of genetic relatedness between different individuals in a family group. It does not have to be a human family, although that is the one we are especially interested in. People are animals. We have exactly the same kind of genetic material as other animals, and share up to 99 per cent of that DNA with our closest relations. We obey the same evolutionary rules as other animals – and even the things that set us apart from our closest relations are not all unique to our species. As we have already seen, people are in the minority in the animal world as a species where the male takes on a degree of responsibility for the offspring. But this is a respectably large minority of species, and for this reason we are also especially interested in the behaviour of birds, where there is a similar sharing of parental responsibility. But in bird or human, or other, species the only way in which an individual can be successful, in terms of evolution, is to leave copies of his or her genes, and to be sure that his or her children have reproduced in their turn. Leaving aside the possibility for doubts about paternity, each parent has a 50 per cent genetic investment in each child – parent and offspring have a genetic relatedness of 0.5. On average, two offspring of the same set of parents also have a relatedness of 0.5. Without going into mathematical details, we can see that in everyday terms each parent 'needs' to raise at least two offspring in order to ensure that all of its own genes are copied, and would 'like' to raise more. Each infant, on the other hand, only really cares about its own survival, although it will be happy to see siblings also doing well, provided that their success is not at its own cost. In other words, the strategy by which a parent can maximize its own reproductive success is not necessarily compatible with the strategy by which the child maximizes its own reproductive success, and, in particular, parents will try to produce more offspring when existing children prefer, in evolutionary terms, to see more attention given to themselves than to new siblings.

At some point, of course, the growing infant becomes able to stand on its own two feet, or fly on its own two wings, and make a living without further parental help. The parent's interests are best served by getting the offspring off her hands (usually it is the mother that is primarily concerned here) as soon as possible and getting on with the job of raising another infant. The offspring's interests are best served by getting the mother – and father if possible – to continue to provide help, or food, as long as possible. But the offspring do share part of the mother's investment in their siblings, so there comes a point where *even in terms of the best strategy for their own genes* it makes better evolutionary sense for them to cut loose from the proverbial apron strings and make their own way in the world, so that the parents can raise more offspring unhindered. Because of the simple relatedness of 0.5 that is involved, each infant should be inclined to seek aid from the parent as long as the cost to the parent – in reproductive terms – is less than half the benefit to the infant. But once the cost to the parent is more than twice the benefit to the offspring, the infant should be willing to leave her to raise another sibling. To the parent, however, the time to start concentrating on the next infant is when the benefit of so doing is *equal* to the cost of continuing to help an older offspring. And therein lies the conflict.

None of this, of course is calculated, neither in people nor in birds. It is all instinctive behaviour, coded in groups of genes and modulated by environmental circumstances that together make animals respond in a certain way to certain stimuli. But over many generations, in both birds and people, genes that code for responses which make infants seek independence at a certain age will spread more widely than those which make infants seek independence too soon or too late, while, similarly, genes that make adults force independence upon their offspring too soon, say, will not spread as widely as those that code for behaviour that makes infants independent a little later in their development.

This simple language sometimes causes confusion by making it seem as if the genes are in some intelligent way directing operations. Perhaps we should stress that complex patterns of behaviour are unlikely to be caused by a single gene or a simple group of genes, but that nevertheless genotypes that provide animals with certain responses to different situations will be selected by evolution and spread. That does not mean that there is 'a gene' for leaving home at, say, 16, which is in competition with 'a gene' for leaving home at 18!

As Daly and Wilson express it, 'what this theory suggests is that there is a stage of conflict that begins at the point where the mother's investment costs her more than it gains her and ends at the point where it costs the young more than it gains them (by virtue of costing the mother twice what it gains them) . . . there is indeed a stage of conflict

165

very like this, and it has a name – weaning.'[2] Weaning, in this sense, can be taken both literally and in a broader sense, applying to the very long period of human childhood and the comparably long period during which the adolescent readies himself, or herself, to leave home. In more general terms, Trivers's theory suggests that any child will always want to get more from its parents than its parents are willing to give.

Of course we have oversimplifed. The situation in the real world is far less clear-cut than this black and white image, and there are biologists who argue that Trivers is completely wrong. Their counter-argument is that genes that express themselves in children in such a way that the child gets more than its fair share of parental investment cannot succeed in the long term, because when the body they inhabit matures and produces children those children will, in turn, extract more parental investment than is good for the parents. Such a mutant form might be imagined as producing families – bird or human – in which a very few children were raised in great comfort while other families were busy raising many offspring in less comfort. And on that picture, the genes that enable the offspring to cheat its parents will soon die out. Such a viewpoint sees the parents as having ultimate control of the situation, since they can, if it comes to the crunch, abandon an over-demanding offspring and start again. That, too, is an extreme, black and white view, which appears to be diametrically opposed to Trivers's argument at its simplest. The truth undoubtedly lies somewhere in between, and finding out just where in the grey area human patterns of behaviour are established is one of the intriguing items of work now in progress. (We find Dawkins' argument, put forward in *The Selfish Gene*, persuasive. He points out that, although siblings may be competing for food, there are complications to their rivalry. An older sibling, for example, may have less urgent need of the food than a younger one, and in some ways may be acting more like a parent by ensuring that the younger sibling does well. If the net cost to brothers and sisters of the eldest grabbing the food is more than twice the benefit he would reap by having the food, then the selfish gene theory says that the eldest should be expected to let them have the food, since there is a 50:50 chance that any of his genes, including the gene for such 'altruism', resides in their bodies as well. This is the kind of 'grey' argument that tells us more about what is going on than either black or white argument.) We can see clear evidence both that there is a genetic tendency for self-restraint in the use of resources within a normal family unit, *and* that parents are not in complete command, by looking at the example of the cuckoo.

Young birds in a typical nest may seem to compete aggressively with their brothers and sisters, with their loud cries and broadly gaping mouths as they beg for food, but the cuckoo takes this to extremes. The female cuckoo lays her egg in a carefully chosen nest built by another species of bird and containing the other bird's eggs. So a young cuckoo hatches from its egg in a nest alongside the eggs laid by a bird of another species, and it has no interest at all in seeing these foster siblings survive, nor has it any direct genetic interest in whether or not its foster parents survive or reproduce. It removes its potential rivals for food by pushing the other eggs out of the nest, and it makes extraordinary demands on the 'parents', working them to exhaustion as they respond blindly to the 'psychological' pressures upon them, the presence of the bird in the nest, its cries and its gape. The example of the cuckoo serves to remind us how genuine offspring are much less selfish than they might be in their demands for parental care, but it also shows us that the parents are conditioned by their evolution to the point where they cannot simply reject the nestling and fly off to raise another brood.

Old Fogies and Young Tearaways

Trivers himself has described his observations of parent–offspring conflict connected with weaning in species as diverse, and geographically far apart, as pigeons living wild in Massachusetts and monkeys in East Africa and India.[3] Young pigeon chicks are fed carefully by both their parents, who bring food to the nest and encourage the chick to feed by stroking its neck with their bill. But when the chicks are almost fully fledged it is they who pounce upon the parents as they return to the roost, demanding food and crowding the parent into a corner. Indeed, says Trivers, he often saw these city dwelling pigeons ignore their almost fledged offspring, and their own nest, to fly instead to some different roosting ledge on a nearby building, to escape this harassment.

Similar incidents happen with langur monkeys and baboons, where it may take several weeks for a mother to break her infant of the habit of demanding milk, or a ride on her back. Studies of these and other species show the broad outlines of the pattern of behaviour predicted by the theory based on kinship, and where more detailed studies can be made they often bear out the theory very accurately. In most cases, it seems that the result of the parent–offspring conflict is that the young get more from their parents than the parents would ideally 'like' to give, but that this is still less than the offspring would 'like' to receive if they had things all their own way. The good old compromise rules.

Trivers also looks at the psychological weapons that the infant has in its armoury, one of which seems to be the temper tantrum, which is no less a feature of chimpanzees (and other primates) than it is of people. A young chimp (or a young human being) in a temper tantrum screams with rage, flings its body to the ground, and bashes itself against hard objects. This is a very alarming procedure for a parent, because there seems to be – and may even genuinely be – a risk of the infant being injured. Parents that fail to respond to a real risk to their offspring will suffer in the evolutionary stakes, so the temper tantrum may trigger the protective parenting that would be a correct response to a real risk to the infant. And in this case the strategy may be as much calculated as it is instinctive. Chimpanzees, as well as human infants, have sometimes been observed, prior to or in the middle of a tantrum, having a quick look round to make sure that their antics will be observed.

Such tantrums should be most common precisely during the period of conflict, what we have called 'weaning' in the broader sense, when the infant still wants parental attention but the parent would be better off investing effort in younger infants. And that is exactly what is seen among chimpanzees, as well as certainly having a familiar ring about it for human parents.

All this has very important implications for the psychological and social sciences, implications which have not, as yet, begun to work their way into the teaching of those disciplines. Conflict between parents and offspring is now seen as inevitable, but for very different reasons than those enshrined in, say, Freudian psychology. Deceit, intentional or instinctive, is also an inevitable part of the generation game, with children pretending to need more from their parents than the parents are willing to give freely. And there is an inbuilt tendency for individuals to act out the roles of their own parents when they become parents themselves, even though they strenuously acted against their own parents when young! Caught in an inevitable evolutionary spiral, today's young tearaways become tomorrow's old fogies, because the best evolutionary strategy for being a successful adolescent is not the same as the best strategy for being a successful parent.

THE PARENTING PUZZLE

Most of the problems of being a parent in the human society we live in occur, as far as parent–offspring conflict goes, when the offspring reach adolescence. The teenage years correspond very closely to the broad definition of 'weaning' as the time when the offspring wants the parents to provide for it but the parents would rather make other use of their resources. In our society, of course, this does not necessarily mean investment in more offspring, although that is still an element. Many people today, child rearing off their hands and still – unlike our counterparts of even a few centuries ago – with many active years ahead of them, would like to take the opportunity to live it up a little and enjoy themselves.

This is a quite new phenomenon, in evolutionary terms, since even for human beings the usual fate of females, in particular, has been to keep reproducing as long as possible and then drop dead from exhaustion. The phenomenon of an extended and healthy middle and old age is still too recent for there to be any clear indications of how our genetic imperatives, selected for quite different ends, will allow us, or encourage us, to respond to this new-found freedom in middle life. But it is certainly interesting that so many people, given the opportunity, behave in ways reminiscent of young, newly mature people – taking holidays, taking up new sports, living more dangerously, and even finding a new sexual partner. It is as if the pattern of behaviour that is triggered by the emergence of a juvenile from the cocoon of family life into independent adulthood can also be triggered by the emergence of an adult individual, or a pair of parents, from the responsibility of family life once the children are raised. And this is just the kind of thing we expect to find in human behaviour – underlying animal patterns, corresponding to our 99 per cent inheritance, deflected into new forms by the results of our one per cent advantage, in this case, by the medical skills that ensure our survival to a ripe old age, combined with the related skills that make it unnecessary for a woman to breed herself to death. Our chance of a 'second adolescence', with all the benefits and none of the drawbacks (not even a nagging parent!), is one of the greatest personal advantages stemming from that one per cent of DNA that makes us uniquely human. Studies of how people behave in their forties and beyond could clearly be fruitful for sociobiologists. But what of the role of the growing teenager in the parent–offspring conflict?

A lot of what we have been saying in this chapter can be crystallized in a paragraph from an article by Glenys Roberts in the London *Standard* on 15 August 1985. Writing on the 'Woman' page, and bemoaning the state of the world in which teenagers 'are dependent long after they are physically grown', she clearly did not appreciate that this is nothing new to modern society but is the pattern down through the ages, in other species as well as our own. But she summed up in a sentence the view of the parent who has made enough investment (from the parent's point of view) and is waiting for the fledgling to leave the nest, even though the fledgling feels that more parental investment is appropriate:

> Faced with a strapping apparition who cannot even be bothered to wash up a cereal bowl, ask yourself who it is that is being exploited.

That is what Trivers's theory of parent–offspring conflict is all about!

David Barash also provides, in *Sociobiology and Behavior*, some examples of behaviour patterns in our close relations that seem to echo familiar human themes. Recall that in the wild the crucial thing from the point of view of both parent and offspring is not the chance to buy a sports car with the money you used to spend on the kids, or using the money to take a world cruise, but simply reproduction. According to Trivers, there inevitably comes a time when mother is ready to have another baby but her existing offspring would do better, genetically speaking, if she concentrated on them. And what we find, says Barash, is that 'immature chimpanzees frequently harass copulating pairs'.[4] Furthermore, 'immature animals responded with particular intensity to their mother's first renewal of sexual behavior following their own birth and suckling.'

Once again, this fits in with the theory; and, once again, we all know of similar examples in human society and in human literature – which, of course, reflects human life. The issue is more clearly focused when we consider the problems that many divorced or single mothers have in getting their young children to accept a new man into the family. In genetic terms, an infant should be even less willing to accept the prospect of the arrival of new babies that have a different father, because they will share only a quarter of the existing infant's genes. Of course, there are also sociological and psychological reasons for a young child to reject its mother's new lover. But counsellors trying to advise a mother in this predicament generally start out from the assumption that the child's jealousy is solely due to the attention that is diverted from the infant to the mother's new partner. Trivers's theory suggests that there is, in addition to this, an in–built 'jealousy' related to the possibility that the mother will produce new babies and lavish attention on these half-siblings while ignoring her existing child.

Again, we must stress that none of this is reasoned out by the child or by the genes. The full scenario would be that children who act in such a way as to prevent their mothers from finding new sexual partners have in the past received more attention from their mothers and therefore their genes, including the ones that make them behave unpleasantly to prospective stepfathers, have spread (the argument runs the same, of course, when applied to step*mothers* as well). Sociobiologists are always urged to take the psychological and social factors into account, and rightly so. But we would urge the psychologists and sociologists to take more account of the biological roots of some of the problems they encounter, in order the better to resolve the conflicts by using the advantages – such as reasoning ability – that we have over those animals that are more blindly directed by their genetic inheritance.

This is, to be fair, beginning to happen. Daly and Wilson have looked at the Canadian statistics on children that are phsyically assaulted – battered – by their parents and find a high proportion of cases in which the 'parent' responsible is a stepfather. This is understandable in sociobiological terms, because the stepfather has no genetic stake in the child, and benefits no more (in those terms) from the child's presence in the family than a cuckoo benefits from the presence of other eggs in the nest. Harsh though it may seem, there can be no doubt that selection has operated, if only to a mild extent in the human line, to favour individuals that are hostile towards prospective step-parents, and simultaneously to favour individuals that are hostile to their stepchildren. And these in-built hostilities still exist, even though in modern society the stepchild may benefit enormously from the arrival on the scene of a new partner for the existing parent, who may be well able to cope with raising the existing child *and* any others that the couple may choose to have – a key new factor, in modern human society, being the element of choice that we have in such matters but which other animals do not.

None of this means that baby battering by stepfathers is either inevitable or natural, let alone desirable. Instead it offers ways to minimize the risk of this happening. If nothing else, armed with this kind of insight, hard-pressed social workers should find it easier to identify families and individuals at risk, and to provide appropriate counselling advice *before* the instinctive hostility between step-parent and stepchild breaks out into damaging conflict.

There are so many examples of the kind of behaviour that Trivers's theory predicts that they would fill a book in their own right. Looking back, again, at our closest relatives, chimpanzee mothers that give birth relatively late in life are invariably more inclined to tolerate the demands of their new infant, which weans late and has the benefit of being carried around for longer than is usual. The underlying reasons for the evolution of this pattern of behaviour are now clear – such a late baby may be the mother's last chance to reproduce, so her best course of action is to secure the existing investment rather than push the infant out into the world and gamble on the slight prospect of getting pregnant again. And although we now have choice and control over whether or not we reproduce again (or at all), human mothers show the same affection and extra care for the child that comes late in life – who does not know a family with an indulged youngest son or daughter?

Older parents and their children suffer less from parent–offspring conflict, not just because the parents are older and wiser, but also because they are more willing to let the children have their way.

But when there is conflict, it will follow the usual pattern. Parents in general will want their children to be less selfish, because to the parent it is a good thing for all the children to be treated equally. Each individual child, however, will tend to be more selfish (and spiteful) than the parents think desirable, because he or she shares only half of his or her genes with even full siblings. This dichotomy actually extends to more distant relatives as well – a child's cousins share only one-eighth of his or her genes, but the child's parents share one-quarter of the genes of what is, to them, a niece or nephew. So it is very broadly true that parents will expect, or want, their children to behave less selfishly to the children they are most likely to come into contact with.

This example is rather nice, since it also shows how biology is subverted by culture. During the many generations that this process was evolving, the children that a child was most likely to come into contact with were indeed siblings, half-siblings, cousins and other relations. So the instinct that has evolved is for parents to encourage children to be nice to their playmates. In the past, this would have helped the spread of copies of the *parents'* genes. Today, those playmates are unlikely to be relations – but the instinct is still there, and we still exhort our offspring to be nice to other kids, share their toys, and so on. We tell ourselves that this is just 'the right way' to do things, and there may be an element of reciprocal altruism involved. But at heart this is rationalization of our automatic behaviour; we are following an instinct that evolved under quite different circumstances.

Parents also want their children to be successful – children represent the investment of the parents' genetic capital in the future, and as the parents get older it gets less and less likely that they will get more chances to reproduce. Teenagers, on the other hand, see their lives stretching out ahead, and want to have a good time while they are young. There will be plenty of time to settle down and raise a family later. So parents inevitably cajole or exhort their children to study hard, to keep out of trouble, not to drink or take drugs, to be nice to other people, and so on. These are all courses of action that would actually improve the immediate prospects of the *parents'* genes being 'looked after' and passed on – they would 'maximize the parents' genetic fitness', in the jargon. We'll leave you to draw you own conclusions about why people behave as they do in your own family. But there is an important, and encouraging, aspect to all of this.

Some people worry about the implications of sociobiology and the concept of the selfish gene, because these ideas revolve around the evolutionary fitness of individuals, and the selection of individuals in competition with one another. As we have seen, this inevitably provides scope for conflict, and the worriers fear that this not only 'explains' human aggression, up to and including war, but makes it inevitable. But we have seen that a tendency for parents to exhort children to be nice to one another, that has evolved for sound 'selfish' reasons, has been channelled by society into a more generally altruistic form, one which our reason tells us must be a good thing. We do not have to go through the sometimes painful process – fatal for many individuals – of evolving a new set of responses to adapt to a changing world, because we can see for ourselves that the right course of action (that is, the one which will bring most benefit to ourselves) is almost always, today, one of cooperation for mutual benefit, with another individual, or group of individuals, or even other nations. The selfishness of our genes may indeed have been partly responsible for bringing us to the edge of nuclear war, because our instinctive responses to conflict situations evolved in circumstances where a stone axe was the ultimate deterrent. But there is every prospect of using the advantage our intelligence and reasoning ability gives us to avoid the ultimate conflict. Indeed, as we shall see, it might all be a mistake anyway.

8
WAR GAMES

Aggression is one of the hardest subjects to tackle in any discussion of sociobiology, because it is so widely misunderstood. The image of 'nature red in tooth and claw' still seems to go hand in hand, in the minds of all too many people, with the idea of evolution by natural selection and survival of the fittest. But, as we have explained, most of the competition in nature involves breeding strategies, not aggression. Certainly there are aggressive species, and ruthless 'warfare' is waged at some levels in the 'struggle for survival'. But these are not the levels at which large mammals like ourselves operate! The most vicious 'aggression' seems to be the prerogative of rather smaller creatures – wasps which lay their eggs in the living flesh of larvae from other species, so that their young will grow up in a ready-made, living food store, or the bugs that invade our own bodies and cause disease. Even the bloodiest of mammals seem noble by comparison, as we recognize in the names we apply to our fellow human beings.

Who, after all, would not be happy to be described as 'lion hearted', 'cat footed', or 'as strong as a bear'? Predators – animals that eat other animals that are smaller and weaker than themselves – are generally respected and held in esteem or awe. But parasites, animals that eat other animals that are larger and more powerful than themselves, are despised. The very name 'parasite' is a term of abuse, while calling a man a louse is asking for trouble. Yet a louse is no less intrinsically courageous than a lion, in its way. Our choice of ephithets tells us as much about ourselves as about the animals whose names we use as labels in this way, and shows that the kind of aggression practised by creatures like lions and bears is something that seems normal in human terms. Clearly, people are, in some sense, aggressive. Warfare and sporting substitutes for warfare are part of our culture, and in order for them to be so there must be something in our genetic inheritance that predisposes us to fit in with this kind of cultural pattern. But, just how aggressive *are* bears and lions?

COWARDLY LIONS

Ecologist Paul Colinvaux has given an insight into the true extent of red teeth and claws in nature in his book *Why Big Fierce Animals are Rare*. Animals, he tells us, come in distinct sizes, with gaps in between. A fox is ten times bigger than the song bird on which it preys; the bird is ten times bigger than the insects it eats; and one of those large insects will be ten times bigger than the mites which are its own prey. This scaling is understood in terms of the need of the predator to be fast enough to catch its prey, and big enough to swallow it, more or less, at a gulp. (Of course, this is an oversimplification. You will have to read Colinvaux's book if you want the detailed subtlety, and an explanation of the (few) exceptions to this rule.) Bigger animals in such a chain are disproportionately less common than smaller animals. You might think, at first guess, that there would be one-tenth as many foxes, say, as there are song birds; but the larger predators are actually much rarer than that. The reason seems to be their need to be able to run fast (or fly, or swim fast) in order to catch their food. Being a predator is an energetic lifestyle that uses up a lot of calories, so each predator needs a large territory over which it hunts for prey.

All the energy in living things on Earth, except for a few strange creatures that live in the murky ocean depths by hot volcanic vents, comes ultimately from the Sun. Plants convert solar energy into what animals regard as food. Many animals eat plants to get their energy, and other animals eat the plant eaters. But at each stage up the chain energy is lost. No conversion process is 100 per cent efficient (quite apart from the energy used up by creatures at each stage in living their own lives), and by the time plant energy has been converted into animal bodies that have in turn been used as food by other animals, there has been a great deal of wastage. So there is a strict limit to how big a predator can

176

be and still be able to eat enough to stay alive, and that limit is at about the size of a tiger, a bear, or a shark. Plant eaters, such as elephants, can grow much bigger than this, because they do not have to run fast to catch their prey – it just sits there, helplessly waiting to be eaten – and also because they are dealing with the basic food source at the bottom of the chain, the next best thing to solar energy itself. And whales, the largest mammals (and largest animals today), cheat by cutting out the middle men. The great baleen whales, as Colinvaux points out, do not eat prey one-tenth their own size. Instead, they use their mouths as sieves, to strain much smaller creatures, the shrimp-like krill, out of the ocean waters by the ton. So they cut out the energy losses that would have been involved if the krill had been eaten by fish, which were eaten by bigger fish, which were eaten by whales!

Colinvaux even has an ingenious explanation for the success of the dinosaur *Tyranosaurus rex*, which many a child's book of dinosaurs will tell you was a big, fierce flesh eater. Big, yes; flesh eater, yes; but fierce, no – according to Colinvaux. It seems that the latest thoughts on the *T. rex* skeleton suggest that it was a rather slow-moving creature, not at all fleet of foot, and that therefore it probably fed on the dead carcases of plant eaters, perhaps finishing off the sick or dying, but not engaging them in fierce combat at all.

This, indeed, gives an insight into the lifestyle of most of the 'fierce carnivores' that are around today. Lions, tigers and the rest generally do pick off the weakest prey animals when they go in search of food. Either the very young or the very old, or the sick, get culled from herds in this way, but only on the rarest occasions is a fit, mature adult pulled down. Predation is really only a glorified form of scavenging. Studies of wolf packs hunting deer or moose show why – if a fit adult male stands and fights, he will be overcome by the pack, but not before he inflicts injuries on some of his attackers. The injured wolves will be unable to hunt with the pack, and will die. So, even though the pack can together bring down a fit adult male, evolution has selected favourably those wolves which choose not to pick on fit adult males, and has selected against those wolves that do. Lions too are, in fact, evolved to be *cowardly*, and never to pick fights with big, strong antelope! There are natural, in-built limits to aggression in the fierce animals that we regard, instinctively, as noble, good role models, and there are similar

177

natural, in-built limits to aggression in human beings. The problems we face today, of course, revolve around the fact that those instincts are based on millions of years of evolution during which people did *not* have access to technological weapons, and so we have to use our intelligence instead of our instincts to decide how much aggression is, in fact, 'worthwhile' today.

TRIBES AND NATIONS

Human aggression exists because it has been selected for in our tribal past. As with other species, we were, before the invention of civilization, predisposed to act aggressively when the likely costs were low and the likely rewards were high, or as a last-ditch, all or nothing response to a perceived threat. When there are only limited resources to be had, aggressive behaviour comes to the fore; and aggression is more likely to be directed towards strangers, according to the inverse of the arguments about kin selection which explain why we have evolved altruistic behaviour towards our nearest and dearest. If it pays to help people you are probably related to, then it also pays to damage the prospects of those you are not related to.

But people can hardly be said to have done much damage to each other's prospects at all, before the advent of modern technological warfare, compared even with the behaviour of the cowardly lion. Edward Wilson stresses the point in his book *On Human Nature*. Those who depict humankind as bloodthirsty in the extreme are simply mistaken. Many studies show that species such as lions, hyenas, and some kinds of monkey go in for fights to the death, infanticide and cannibalism to a far greater extent than any human society. 'If hamadryas baboons had nuclear weapons,' says Wilson, 'they would destroy the world in a week'[1] – which rather suggests that, since we have lived with nuclear weapons for four decades, we are models of restraint and caution, by some animal standards! The cultural evolution of aggression, Wilson sums up, involves a genetic predisposition towards learning some form of cultural aggression, moulded by the prevailing environmental conditions and by the history of the particular group that an individual belongs to, which biases it towards one cultural option rather than another. Within those constraints, people have fought in circumstances where fighting may increase their own genetic success, or that of close relations – the cry 'for King and country' is precisely explained in sociobiological terms.

Investigations of non-technological societies have shown that human aggression typically involves only minor amounts of fighting, with only occasional injuries and even rarer deaths. Individuals who do well in battle (if these skirmishes really qualify for the term battle) certainly do well, in evolutionary terms, by gaining status, wives and property. Those who do badly, however, are scarcely any worse off than they were before. So the selection pressures which maintain this modest amount of aggression are clear, and just as in other species (male red deer competing for mates, or whatever it might be) threats and bluff are all important, while there are clear signals of submission which are used by the losers to break off hostilities before they suffer irreparable harm. The archetypal society of the North American Indians is as good an example of this as any; before the arrival of white Europeans, 'warfare' among the tribes was so ritualized that in many cases no attempt was made to kill opponents, but great prestige was gained by a warrior who 'counted coup' by touching his opponents in the thick of battle. Such a 'chivalrous' attitude did not stand the natives in good stead against the invaders.

But why did the Europeans invade North America at all? What are the pressures which can cause human aggression to spill over and to override the checks and balances provided by evolution? The answer seems to lie in a combination of technology – shooting a man at long range with a rifle is sufficiently remote that any instinctive compassion cannot take control – and population growth. Paul Colinvaux has worked out a detailed, and controversial, theory along these lines, which purports to explain most of the history of civilization in ecological terms. His argument is not universally accepted, but certainly provides some food for thought.[2]

The argument builds from the evidence that people are unlike other animals in being able to calculate in advance how many infants they are likely to be able to raise to maturity. But, like all other species on Earth, we have an in-built drive to raise as many offspring as possible – any species that did not carry this biological imperative in its genes has long since lost out in the evolutionary stakes. Every other species occupies a definite place in the ecological web, a niche. There is a niche for foxes, a niche for elephants, one for song birds, and so on. Each niche has room for a certain number of inhabitants, and if more are produced, for whatever reason, then they will die. A hundred million years ago, there were much the same sort of niches available to life on Earth as there are today, but many were filled by dinosaurs. There were dinosaur equivalents of cattle and birds, foxes and sheep. It was only after the dinosaurs died out, as a result of environmental changes, that the way was open for new species to move in and take over these empty niches, and the ones that did so successfully, radiating out in many different forms from a stock of small species that had almost literally lived under the feet of the dinosaurs, were the mammals. The niches were still much the same, so the mammals that evolved and adapted to fill them became very similar in their lifestyles to the dinosaurs that had preceded them.

But people are different. Perhaps our greatest advantage over other species is our versatility, our ability to adapt to different niches, or even to invent new niches for ourselves. People are unspecialists.

Colinvaux makes the point by drawing an analogy with professions. The 'niche' of aeronautical engineer has a certain number of places in it, and the number of places depends on the size of the aircraft industry. If schools and colleges decide to train more people to be aeronautical engineers, it does not follow that they will all find jobs. The surplus will have to re-train in some other field and find work elsewhere. People, says Colinvaux, have always adjusted their numbers to match the resources available – either by infanticide or by social customs which limit sexual activity, our ancestors made sure that they raised the maximum number of children that could be fed, but did not attempt to raise too many children. That would have been counterproductive, as resources would be spread too thin for any to survive. When first agriculture and then the various technological revolutions came along, the immediate effect was to make people rich, with more resources available for the old, small population. But the second result, he says, was that people instinctively adjusted their 'breeding strategy' to produce more adult heirs to take advantage of the new opportunities. So populations boomed, while at the same time expectations had been raised. And when the new resources, or technologies, came under pressure from a rising population, then it was natural for our ancestors to turn to new lands, as the Europeans did when they moved into North America, in order to maintain the higher standard of living for as many people as possible for as long as possible.

This is a very interesting thesis, which gives a new look at historical events such as the rise and fall of the Roman Empire. It also, perhaps, tells us something about the way people behave in modern societies. Poor people, says Colinvaux, have much lower expectations than rich people, and it takes less in the way of resources to maintain a person in poverty than in affluence. So, in modern society, even with the availability of contraceptives and abortion, and in spite of anything that they may say (or even believe) to the contrary, poor people will instinctively raise large families. This is a 'good thing' in terms of success of their genes, since they will leave many offspring (even if those offspring live in poverty) to have children in their turn. Rich people, however, have to make a bigger investment in their children in order to be sure that their offspring will be able to maintain their lifestyle. Many years of education make raising each child a long process, and the cost of the process restricts the resources available for other children. So the 'correct' evolutionary strategy for the affluent is to have a few children that are each set carefully on the road to success. And this, says Colinvaux, is why the wealthy have smaller families than the poor.

As populations increase, resources are spread more thinly and society becomes more restrictive, hedging people around with rules and regulations in order to maintain a reasonable standard for all. Perhaps being deliberately provocative, Colinvaux suggests that the Soviet Union, with an educated but small population and a very large landmass rich in mineral resources, 'ought' to be a haven of liberty and freedom, and probably will be within the next 50 to 100 years, while the United States, having already used up resources such as oil and with an increasing population could follow the path towards bureaucratic totalitarianism. But there *ought* to be no reason for either superpower to attack the other, because the logic of nuclear war dictates that there could be no winner – and superior logic is one of the most important features of our one per cent advantage over the apes. ('superior' only in the sense that we can work out longer chains of cause and effect than our hairy ape cousins; yet again, we see that what separates us from the other apes is only a matter of degree. In this case, the computers in our heads are bigger than theirs, and can handle more complex chains of reasoning, but seem to run on the same basic rules.)

'The worst prospect we have to face', says Colinvaux, 'is that the freest of us will lose our liberty from a remorseless and gentle jostling of crowds of people.' But this need not happen, because 'we are human, understandable, and very different from other animals. We breed in human and controllable ways. We can change our life styles to let women do more useful things than raise surplus children. Because we can work out what is happening to us, we need fear neither our future nor our fate.'[3] But how, then, can we possibly have been so stupid as to get ourselves into a nuclear arms race, threatening a war which nobody can win? As we said at the end of chapter 7, it seems that it is all a mistake, the result of the workings of an evolutionary strategy which may be stable in the mathematical sense but which has been distorted by the unusual circumstances confronting humankind today.

THE PRISONER'S DILEMMA

We learned about the games theory approach to an understanding of the nuclear arms race through the work of P. G. Bennett and M. R. Dando, a contact stemming from a spell one of us spent working at the Science Policy Research Unit at the University of Sussex. Games theory, of course, grew up in the context of modern warfare and simulations of modern warfare and political strategies, and later moved sideways into the study of evolution, where it has developed in parallel for more than 20 years now. The more strictly biological ESS approach has a great deal to tell us about the way individuals should behave towards one another, and this, as we shall see, is relevant to the way nations behave towards one another. But let us start with the aspect of political games theory that we learned first, a version of the problem that is known as the 'prisoner's dilemma', in the context of present-day international politics.

One of the most important lessons of games theory is that even if everyone is agreed on the most desirable course of action – for example, nuclear disarmament – a collection of individuals or nations acting independently of each other may find it difficult to achieve the most desirable aims. As we saw in the hawks vs doves scenario, the ESS need not be the one that would bring most benefit to most individuals – the catch is that the only way all individuals could benefit from the best possible strategy is for all to agree in advance to pursue that strategy, and to stick by the agreement. 'Prisoner's dilemma' illustrates the problem.

The basic scenario can be found in all the standard texts, and here we follow the version in *Game Theory and Politics*, by Steven Brams (Macmillan, 1975). Imagine two criminals, partners in crime, who are arrested and placed in separate cells with no means of communication with each other. The District Attorney believes the prisoners to be guilty of a serious crime, but has no proof that will stand up in court. He needs a confession, and attempts to gain one by telling each prisoner in turn that he will offer them a deal. If one suspect confesses and implicates the other, who does not confess, the confessor will go free as a reward for cooperation, while the other will get sent down for the maximum sentence, ten years. If both confess then, since the DA can hardly set them both free, each will get a lighter sentence, maybe three years. And if neither confesses, both the prisoners and the DA know that all he can nail them with is a lesser crime for which the maximum penalty is a year in prison.

The actual numbers are not important, but they serve to illustrate the dilemma. If each prisoner can trust the other not to confess, then the best overall deal is for the two of them to remain silent. But if one prisoner suspects that the other might rat on him, it is better to confess, even though if both confess that will result in a bigger jail sentence than if neither confesses. Confession is the strategy which *minimizes* the *maximum* jail sentence the prisoner can receive, and this mini–max strategy is the best one, even though it ensures that the prisoner cannot receive the lowest possible sentence allowed by the game, one year for the lesser offence.

In this simple example, there is an obvious resolution of the dilemma. The prisoners can agree in advance never to confess under any circumstances. But who will hold them to the pact? The 'no confession' rule is allegedly one enforced by the Mafia; in that case the dilemma is removed because each prisoner knows that if the other confesses and is released a worse punishment will be enforced outside. Unfortunately, there is no 'super superpower' around to enforce any nuclear disarmament pacts the USA and USSR might sign. If one suspects that the other is tempted by the offer of freedom, the dilemma is back in full force. Bennett and Dando, among others, have explained the arms race in terms of a modified prisoner's dilemma scenario. Each side might genuinely wish to disarm but dare not do so for fear of the consequent aggression by the other side. Even with genuinely peace-loving 'players' in the game, the strategy that minimizes the worst thing that can happen to you (the mini–max strategy) may still be to arm to the teeth and be ready to ward off aggression. And this is why.

The situation is complicated because there may be a difference between the wishes of each nation and what the opposing nation *perceives* as its wishes. This brings us into the arena of hypergame theory, where the rules are different because each player sees the game differently. Genuinely peace-loving 'players' who understand each other would have no difficulty reaching a stable conclusion for the game in which both have disarmed. But if each suspects the other of evil intent, then fear of being tricked into a position of inferiority maintains the arms race – and hypergame theory can put all this on a mathematical basis, in a rather exact analogy with the classic prisoner's dilemma 'game'.[4]

So the present perilous state of the world may have resulted not from aggressive intent, nor from stupidity on the part of our leaders, but from a misunderstanding that can now be explained in a scientific fashion. The question 'what price are we prepared to pay to deter the aggressor?' has been the overriding one in superpower politics, even though neither side need necessarily actually be an aggressor, and the situation is more like what Bennett and Dando graphically call 'mutual paranoia'. Understanding the situation is at least halfway to getting rid of the misconceptions and finding out whether the other guy is really serious about wanting to disarm. The mathematical analysis suggests that each side should at the very least respond to overtures made by the other, if only to see how far that gets us down the road to peace. And this commonsense conclusion is very much borne out by the application of ESS theory in general, and the prisoner's dilemma in particular, to individual evolution.

The Safety of Tit-for-Tat

In *Social Evolution*, Robert Trivers draws an analogy between games theory of the prisoner's dilemma and reciprocal altruism. Altruism is, after all, the mirror image of aggression, so it is no surprise to find the same mathematical rules effective as an aid to understanding both situations. In this case, the dilemma is whether or not to cooperate with another individual. If I offer him help and he takes it but does not help me, I lose out; but if we help each other, both gain. What is the stable strategy in such a situation? Is it best to cooperate, or to cheat by pretending to cooperate but only taking help, or what? Should my course of action always be the same, or should I modify it in the light of the response I get from other people? Robert Axelrod and William Hamilton investigated the possibilities by using computer models of this variation of the dilemma. In much the same way that computer chess programs are set up to compete against one another in tournaments, Axelrod and Hamilton took 14 different strategy models, plus some that 'played' at random, and ran them through 200 cycles of the game in a computer. It turned out that the strategy which scored best overall was the simplest, which is called tit-for-tat. It has only two rules: on the first move of the game, cooperate; afterwards, do exactly what your opponent did last time. Tit-for-tat, says Trivers, is 'a strategy of cooperations based on reciprocity'.

A second round of competition involving 62 entries, most of them designed to meet the challenge of beating tit-for-tat, and a total of three million choices run in the computer came up with the same result, confirming the superiority of tit-for-tat in an environment where strategies compete against one another. Tit-for-tat wins hands down, especially when refined so that it will 'forgive' just one unfriendly act, turning the other cheek and offering cooperation once more before resorting to copying the other player's approach. In the animal world, this is equivalent to saying that animals following the tit-for-tat strategy would have an advantage sufficient to wipe the evolutionary floor with the others. It is an ESS with a vengeance, and no competing strategy can displace it once it has become established.

This has profound implications for everyday life, as well as for big power politics. There is no doubt that reciprocal altruism has been an important feature of our own evolution, and we have ideas of morality and fair play, friendship and gratitude, which are best seen as mechanisms that have evolved to control reciprocal altruism in the most advantageous way for the individual. Since we all evolved under the same evolutionary pressures, and we share the same basic gene pool it is a reliable rule of thumb in life to apply the tit-for-tat strategy in your interactions with other people – cooperate the first time you interact, and then follow your 'partner's' example for future 'moves' in the 'game'. In other words, 'do as you would be done by,' at first, and then respond in kind. The result is that most people, most of the time, cooperate with each other and get along fine.

So what can this tell us about superpower politics? Politicians are just people, and the same rules apply to them as to other people. Even if we personify each superpower as one player in a supergame of prisoner's dilemma, the rules are still the same. The correct strategy in the arms race is (1) offer to cooperate with the other guy in reducing arms and (2) follow his example on all subsequent moves. It is now easier than ever to see how we got ourselves into this mess. In the unusual circumstances following World War Two, neither of the new power blocs trusted the other, even though they had just been working together to defeat a common enemy. The mere fact of the existence of new superweapons was enough to induce paranoia, and the 'game' went wrong at the first step. Ever since, each side has been faithfully, and correctly in terms of the strategy, following the tit-for-tat rule on the up escalator. But if someone had the initiative to take one of the olive branches offered by the other side at face value, it would be just as easy to reverse the process, and proceed on the down escalator by a series of cautious, graded, tit-for-tat *dis*armaments. Offer to cooperate and then follow the other guy's lead is the best rule for each new player in the game, and we have nothing to lose by taking the offer of cooperation made by the latest player in the game on the Soviet side, Mikhail Gorbachev, at face value – just as his predecessors would have lost nothing by accepting the overtures made by previous incumbents of the White House. Will we have the collective sense to use the advantage we have over the apes, our logical intelligence, to resolve the dilemma? We can only hope that the message gets through to the right quarters, for surely only a tyrant would really want to maintain the present state of global tension. And although that tension may have been partly built up by just such people, as Gandhi reminded us, 'there have been tyrants and murderers, but in the end they always fall', Tyranny is not an ESS for the human species; reciprocal altruism is. And there lies our best hope.

APPENDIX
ARE APES DESCENDED FROM MAN?

In 1985, Masami Hasegawa, Hirohisa Kishino and Taka-aki Yano published the latest, and seemingly most accurate, datings of the human-ape splitting derived from the molecular clock technique. According to this study, the date of the split may have been as recent as 2.7 million years ago. As the Japanese researchers summed up their finding, 'although there is some uncertainty in the clock, this dating may pose a problem for the widely believed hypothesis that the bipedal creature *Australopithecus afarensis*, which lived some 3.7 million years ago at Laetoli in Tanzania and at Hadar in Ethiopia, was ancestral to man and evolved after the human-ape splitting.'[1] One possible explanation of the similarity between human and chimp DNA, say Hasegawa and colleague, is that DNA was transferred through hyridization between a proto-human and a proto-chimpanzee after the former had developed bipedalism.

But there is another alternative. Perhaps *A. Afarensis* – Lucy – lived before the human-ape split. In that case, her uprightwalk would be a characteristic which chimpanzees lost, and in that sense recent chimpanzee (and gorilla) evolution may have proceeded from a recognizably proto-human form towards the modern ape form. In simple language, apes may be descended from man, or a least from proto-man, We were delighted to see this possibility aired in the 1985 paper by the Japanese team, because, as they explicitly acknowledge in that paper, the hypothesis was first suggested by one of us, in collaboration with Jeremy Cherfas.

We developed the idea in the light of Don Johanson's discovery of

A. afarensis, as described in his book *Lucy*, written in collaboration with Maitland Edey. Johanson tells how he agonized over whether to place Lucy as the earliest known member of the *Homo* line or as a member of the closest fossil relations to *Homo*, *Australopithecus*. Eventually, he settled on a family tree which has Lucy at about 3.5 million years ago, followed by a fork in the tree. One branch leads to *Homo habilis* at about 2 million years ago, and on to *H. erectus* and ourselves. The other branch leads to the australopithecines, *A. africanus* and *A. robustus*, contemporaries of each other and of the ancestral forms of *Homo*. Conventional wisdom amongst palaeontologists and zoologists is that neither of these two australopithecines has left living descendants today, even though they were around in Africa as recently as one million years ago. But is the conventional wisdom right? You have probably already gauged our drift, but here is the detailed argument, almost exactly as it was first aired in an article by John Gribbin and Jeremy Cherfas in *New Scientist* on 3 September 1981 (vol. 91, p. 592); it was later elaborated on in *The Monkey Puzzle* (see Bibliography).

The best evidence there is – the only direct evidence, in fact – suggests that man, the chimpanzee and the gorilla shared a common ancestor less than 4.5 million years ago. This is completely at odds with the traditional story derived from palaeontology. The fossil story – as usually told – has a creature called *Ramapithecus* as the first hominid, the first member of man's own line that is distinct from the line that leads to modern apes. And *Ramapithecus* flourished from 14 to 8 million years ago. Then there is a yawning gap from eight to four million years ago, all the known hominid fossils from this period rattling disconsolately in a small cardboard box. After the gap there is Johanson's famous Lucy, walking upright but with a primitive ape-like skull, around 3.75 million years ago. The implication is that the split between man and the apes happened sometime before the first *Ramapithecus*, at least 14 million years ago. Admittedly *Ramapithecus* has lately begun to fade from prominence even in the palaeontological story, but still the consensus of informed opinion puts the origin of man's line no more recent than ten million years ago, and most people, despite the misgivings of a few palaeoanthropologists, still go for a very ancient origin for man.

However, there are no fossils that are clearly ancestors of the chimpanzee or gorilla but not of man. There are contenders, it is true, most notably *Dryopithecus* and its kin, the 'woodland apes' of 20 million years ago, but nothing that can unequivocally be said to be an ancestor of any modern ape and not of man. So the traditional story is playing with conjecture when it comes to the origin of man's line, and that conjecture does not account for observations by biochemists and immunologists – observations which show that proteins and genes (DNA) of apes and man are remarkably similar; much more similar, in fact, than they would be if apes and man had indeed diverged as early as the palaeontologists suggest. There is the further puzzle posed by anatomy, which is also strikingly similar in man and apes.

Picture an orang-utan or a chimpanzee climbing through the trees; now imagine a human gymnast on the parallel bars, the rings, or the horizontal bar. Think of a chimpanzee brandishing a branch as it mock charges an intruder; and a human about to throw a javelin. Think, quite simply, of getting up in the morning and stetching. All these activities, and plenty of others, reflect the very special torso shaped by natural selection to enable its owner to hang below branches and to stretch sideways – the activity known as brachiation. It is the upper body that sets the apes apart from the monkeys, and it its the upper body that makes apes seem so 'human'.

It is quite easy to imagine the selective forces that produce this arm-swinging set of adaptations. With them, animals can be securely positioned with their centre of gravity below a whippy branch and reach out sideways to grab the fruit that is generally so abundant at the tips of the branches. It is not so easy to explain why man and the apes should share these peculiarities. Normally when two animals share a particular feature it is for one of two reasons. Either they share a common ancestor, as in the case of the elephant and the rock hyrax – which look remarkably different at first sight (the latter looks like a large guinea-pig), but which both have unusual and similar feet – or the feature is a response to a peculiar set of circumstances that dictate a particular evolutionary solution. This is examplified by the tuna, the shark and the porpoise, which have very similar shapes even though they belong to quite different classes of animal, with quite separate origins.

So the anatomical similarities of man and apes could have come about because they share a common ancestor, or they could be the result of so-called parallel evolution. The problem, for the palaeontologists, is that they lack the evidence to decide. The dryopithecine fossil apes that pre-date the proposed split with man possess none of the specializations needed for brachiation. And yet all the modern apes have these specializations. The most reasonable explanation is that at some stage in the past all the modern apes shared a common, brachiating ancestor. Man, who allegedly split from the apes before the apes had become brachiators, also carries the marks of a brachiators. But, say the palaeontologists, he does not have a brachiating ape as ancestor. His similarities to the other apes result from parallel evolution over some 15 million years.

This is all a bit hard to assimilate, not least because what little we know of *Ramapithecus* indicates that it obtained its diet on the ground and hence was terrestrial rather than a tree-dweller. If *Ramapithecus*, the putative first hominid, was not a tree-dweller, when did the hominid line develop its brachiating specializations?

The molecules provide an answer. If man and the African apes split less than 4.5 million years ago, they shared a common ancestor who was a brachiator. But the molecules do not provides a complete scenario for the transition from tree-swinging ape to upright walking Lucy, or indeed to chimpanzee. That is what we aim to provide here.

The most accomplished brachiators, the gibbons and the orang-utan, live exclusively in the forests of Asia, and we know that they split from the line leading to man and the African apes ten and eight million years ago respectively. So it is reasonable to suppose that the first brachiators arose some time before ten million years ago, and that they did so in Asia. This brachiator would be a descendant of *Dryopithecus*, but would definitely not be *Ramapithecus*, which is almost certainly a dead end. At one time, the middle of the Miocene, the climate was warm and there was a lush carpet of forest over much of Europe, Africa and the Middle East and Asia, so our brachiator would have found ample opportunity to make a living. Indeed it seems likely that the dryopithecines adapted to various environments and so evolved into several new groups. This kind of diversification is called 'adaptive radiation'. Some of the dryopithecines took to life on the ground, and these are the ramapithecines, not only *Ramapithecus* itself but also its close relatives *Sivapithecus* and *Gigantopithecus*. Others took to a lifestyle spent in the trees; these are the brachiators on whom we shall concentrate. And quite probably there were other offshoots of the dryopithecines that specialized in different ways of life that biologists have yet to discover.

Gigantopithecus managed to survive until about half a million years ago, but *Ramapithecus* and *Sivapithecus* were extinct by eight million years ago. Of all the participants in the dyropithecine radiation, only one group survived until the present day: the brachiators.

The gibbon split from the main brachiating line ten million years ago, and developed brachiation to perfection. Long arms, a short body and legs, and a remarkable agility give the gibbon the ability to fly through the forest canopy without ever seeming to pause for a grip. The orang-utan arose slightly later, eight million years ago, and developed a different approach, becoming as agile in the hind legs as the gibbon is in its arms. The gibbon is a sprinter, the orang-utan is a gymnast that is really a four-armed creature, suspended among the branches like an orange spider and using whichever limb is handiest to grab the nearest succulent fruit.

The next major split on the line takes place 4.5 million years ago, or perhaps slightly more recently. The results of that split are found only in Africa, so we may assume that Africa is where the split took place. Sometime between eight million years ago, when the orang-utan diverged, and 4.5 million years ago, when the apes and man diverged, the brachiating ape made the journey from Asia to Africa. But by this time, towards the end of the Miocene period, the climate was becoming more severe and the forests were beginning to dwindle. Quite probably this shrinking of the habitat produced competition that favoured animals that could make a living elsewhere. But because of the changing climate there was probably no forest to connect Asia and Africa – which poses another problem. How did an arm swinging tree-dweller travel 8000 km with no trees to swing from?

The answer of course is that it walked. Probably not upright on two legs, though the possibility cannot be discounted, but on all fours. Brachiating, aside from bringing tasty fruits at the ends of branches within reach, also fits an animal remarkably well for walking more or less upright. The torso hangs vertically much of the time, and this promotes anatomical changes that make walking much easier (that is, evolutionary changes, that make for successful brachiators also make for competent walkers). Of course, the kind of walking we see today in chimps, gorillas or orang-utans is nothing like upright bipedalism. They can walk on two legs, but only with an inefficient rolling gait that quickly tires them out. More usually they walk on the two hind legs but support some of the weight on one or both of their arms. This type of locomotion is called knuckle walking, because the fingers are turned under so that the knuckles take the weight. A baboon walking on all fours places its palms flat on the ground; if an ape, whose hands and arms have been modified to swing below branches, tried this it would tend to force the bones of its lower arms through its wrist. The only solution is to curl the fingers and use knuckles to bear the load. Knuckle walking is not inefficient, and it is easy to imagine an animal like a chimpanzee making a long overland journey in this way.

Of course it was not a single group of apes that set out to walk from Asia to Africa. As with their human descendants who eventually spread from their birthplace in Africa to colonize the globe, a slow progression of just 30 km in each generation would have taken them between the two continents in a few thousand years, and that kind of travel is easily achieved by the natural spacing of animals in search of unexploited habitat. Indeed, members of the other dryopithecine branch (including *Ramapithecus*) got to Africa even earlier, but if they were already eating a ground-dweller's diet 14 million years ago they were probably well adapted to a four-footed life on the ground and could have made the trip with ease.

Once in Africa, say six million years ago, the knuckle walker would have discovered further pockets of forest along the river banks in quite large patches. There it would be free to take to the trees again, for there were no other brachiating primates with which to compete. But the forests were still shrinking, and especially if there had been a population explosion when the knuckle walker rediscovered the forests, the screws were inexorably tightened. For whatever reasons – and collecting food to share, with all that that entails for the growth of society, was surely among them – efficient upright walking became an advantage. By 3.75 million years ago we have Don Johanson's incontrovertible evidence of an upright ape, *Australopithecus afarensis* –

that is, Lucy. She and her kinfolk were certainly successful inhabitants of the plains, probably setting up camps by fresh water and going on expeditions to gather food.

So the brachiating line has, at last, produced a true walker. What of the other two branches? Around four million years ago, after the long drought that marked the end of the Pliocene period, the climate began to change for the better. There was more rain, the forests began to spread from their beleaguered positions, there was more fruit to eat, and so on. To some of Lucy's descendants this was of little interest; they had made their choice and were doing very nicely, thank you, on the plain. It was a hard life, but one that the rapid explosion in brain power was making easier. But what would have become of any proto-humans tempted by the sybaritic life, sitting in or under trees and munching on fruits and vegetables? Such a life would hardly be likely to stimulate the development of the brain, and with an abundance of goodies to hand there would be no pressure to cooperate and share food. Without the need to share food and rely on one another, what use is a complex society? You can see where we are going; chimp and gorilla we argue, are the remnants of two lines that gave up the hard life on the plains and returned to the comfort of the trees, and they did so after proto-man had taken quite a few steps on the road to humanity.

In the popular mind, man is descended from chimpanzee. This is not true. Both are descended from some common ancestor, and when pressed the popular mind would admit that what it really thinks is that man and the chimp are descended from something very ape-like, very like a chimp. To translate our suggestion into that form of speech, we think that the chimp is descended from man, that the common ancestor of the two was much more man-like than ape-like. Whatever the small genetic changes needed to accomplish the anatomical reshufflings that produced the upright ape, they could surely have been equally easily reversed.

There is no fossil evidence to contradict this view, only modern anatomy. This, we admit, suggests that the pelvis of the chimpanzee is that of a primitive knuckle-walking brachiator rather than a one-time biped who reverted to arm swinging and knuckle walking. In our defence, we would counter that perhaps the reversion has been absolutely perfect, that perhaps the genetic changes that produced early man from an ape were cleanly reversed to produce early chimps and gorillas from man.

Our modest proposal may seem like a wild flight of fancy, the over-vivid imaginings of two armchair anthropologists with no experience of palaeoanthropology in the field. Certainly we would not want to defend it to the death, but the very fact that it is entirely within the confines of the evidence that we have points up the frailty of the conventional history of man and apes. And we can perhaps cloak it in respectability by phrasing it in terms of the story that Don Johanson, one of the world's two most prominent palaeoanthropologists, has to tell about his most startling discovery, the 3.75 million year old Lucy and other remains from the Hadar region of Ethiopia.

Johanson describes, in his book *Lucy*, the key insight, the blinding flash of light that made him see how the Hadar fossils, including Lucy, could be slotted into place. This was the realization that the teeth of the fossils on the *Homo* line had changed very little over the period from three to two million years ago. Before, along with other palaeo-anthropologists, Johanson had been working on the assumption that large teeth were more 'primitive' (that is, older) and that fossils with smaller teeth must be more recent, the evolutionary response to a changing diet. 'I now saw', says Johanson, 'that what I had taken for a late human trait was actually a primitive one. A better word here would be old, because primitive suggests something less good, less highly evolved, whereas in truth it may be perfectly good' (p. 277). Once he had realized that the teeth of fossils on the main *Homo* line at this time had changed very little – presumably because they were well adapted to the diet of our ancestors and had no need to change – Johanson saw that the fossil record showed that only the teeth of our cousin hominids, the australopithecines, had altered. 'They had gone in a direction of their own,' he explains, 'to satisfy a lifestyle somewhat different from that being lived by early humans – a lifestyle that would have become increasingly specialized and lead to the development of larger and larger teeth' (p. 278).

Lucy and her kind become, on this picture, the ancestor common both to *Homo* and *Australopithecus* lines, the last of our non-*Homo* ancestors. This sets the date of the oldest human ancestor as some time after Lucy, less than 3.5 million years ago, but Johanson does not openly suggest that the split he dates so neatly to almost the same time as that indicated by the molecular clocks is the same as the split between man and apes. Why not? We have no idea. Perhaps because everyone 'knows' that the man–ape split occurred 20 million years ago.

Let us look more closely at the evidence. The *Australopithecus* lines that descended from a Lucy-like ancestor were around until about a million years ago, according to the fossil remains so far unearthed. These cousins of ours, living in the same part of the world as early man but not members of the same species, walked upright and came in two varieties, *A. robustus* (1.25–1.5 m tall but not very athletic looking) and the smaller *A. Africanus* (less than 1.25 m tall and more slender). They are sometimes referred to as the robust and gracile australopithecines respectively. 'For about a million years,' says Johanson, 'they appear to have walked side by side' with *Homo* but 'by one million [years ago] there were no australopithecines left. They had all become extinct' (p. 285).

There are no more fossils, it is true, but is Johanson's assumption that the australopithecines had become extinct justified? Gaps of a million years in the fossil record are far from uncommon, and one of Johanson's great hopes for renewed fieldwork in Ethiopia is that he may find fossils from what he describes as a 'black hole', a 'pall of ignorance' in palaeontology covering the period from three to two million years ago (p. 360). Suppose we say that rather than *Australopithecus* becoming extinct one million years ago there is a 'pall of ignorance' over his subsequent evolution. What might he have evolved into? The best guess is again based on those teeth. Alan Walker, at Johns Hopkins University in Baltimore, has been using an electron microscope to study the miniscule scratches, grooves and pits in the teeth of various living species and relates these markings to the animal's diet. Then he can look at the markings on fossil teeth and make inferences about what the fossils were eating. Johanson describes Walker's work, and its startling implications as follows:

> The polishing effect [Walker] finds on the teeth of robust australopithecines and modern chimpanzee indicates that australopithecines, like chimps, were fruit eaters. That news came as a surprise. Everything we have learned about australopithecines – that they were ground-dwelling, bipedal, savanna-frequenting

creatures – suggests that they were omnivores ... if they were primarily fruit eaters, as Walker's examination of their teeth suggests they were, then our picture of them, and of the evolutionary path they took is wrong' (p. 358).

Perhaps our armchair speculations can help Johanson resolve his dilemma. For, accepting Walker's evidence at face value, the split from a Lucy-like ancestor into two or more branches of hominid exactly fits our picture of one branch of the family giving up the difficult business of becoming human and settling to a luxurious life of ease.

However, as someone once said, 'there is no such thing as a free lunch'; the price the australopithecines paid for theirs was that they abandoned the opportunity to become human. They became more ape-like, a term that may annoy the professional palaeontologists but whose meaning will be clear to everyone. Could they, indeed, have become so ape-like that they are represented today by the chimpanzee and the gorilla? The fit with lifestyle and with timings of the molecular clock is so impressive that the idea has to be taken seriously as a basis for discussion, even though there are problems with hip structure and so on. As Johanson has made clear, there are even bigger problems, it seems, with the conventional view of *Australopithecus*.

The puzzle is one that fans of Sherlock Holmes will appreciate. On the one hand we have two related species, large and small variations on the theme, that split with the human line, from their common ancestor, roughly 3.5 millions years ago and were fruit eaters. We can trace their existence in the fossils to one million years ago. On the other hand we have two hairy apes living in Africa today, both close relatives of the human line, from which they split less than 4.5 million years ago, and both of them, too, are fruit eaters. Furthermore, palaeontologists will tell you that no fossils ancestral to the modern chimp and gorilla have been found. So we have two living species, without known ancestors, and two fossil species, without known descendants, and all four are closely related to man and eat the same things. As Johanson says of his fossil teeth, quoting Euclid with obvious approval, 'things that are equal to the same thing are equal to each other' (p. 227), And as Holmes said, once you have eliminated the impossible, what remains, however improbable, is the truth.

Is there any other fossil evidence to support our speculations? In his book *The Making of Mankind*, Richard Leakey mentions the work of Ralph Holloway, an anthropologist at Columbia University, New York, who has deduced the nature of the brains of our ancestors from studies of the interiors of fossil skulls. 'The basic shape of the human brain', says Holloway (Leakey, p. 131), 'is clearly evident in the hominids of *at least* two million years ago.' This, says Leakey, was a surprise for palaeontologists, 'as the size of the australopithecine brain was not dramatically different from that of a chimp or gorilla brain'. From our point of view, this is no surprise at all.

The principle of Ockham's razor demands that the simplest explanation should be preferred to the more complicated; and the principle surely advises us that the simplest assumption, until proof to the contrary turns up, is that the two ancient hominids that split from the human line at the end of the Pliocene, and left fossil remains right up to a million years ago, are the ancestors of our closest relations alive on Earth today. Why not?

We do not say dogmatically that the modern chimpanzee and gorilla are the descendants of the two *Australopithecus* lines; we do suggest that this possibility resolves so many aspects of the evolutionary puzzle that it should at least be taken seriously and not dismissed out of hand by the experts. Johanson's own experience with Lucy and the australopithecine teeth indicates the need to keep an open mind on such issues until proof is conclusive.

A final irony is that Johanson, unlike ourselves, may well have held the solution to this problem in his hands. His colleague Tim White has painstakingly reconstructed a composite skull of *A. afarensis*, Lucy's species, from the fragmentary remains of several individuals. 'It looked', Johanson tells us (p. 357), 'like a small female gorilla.'

NOTES

CHAPTER 1

1. Susman (ed.), *The Pygmy Chimpanzee*, p. xii.
2. R. Yerkes, *Almost Human*, Century, New York, 1925
3. Quoted recently by, for example, Adrienne Zihlman in Susman (ed.), *The Pygmy Chimpanzee*, p. 179.
4. R. Lewin, *Science*, 226 (1984) p. 1179.
5. A. Zihlman, V. Sarich, J. E. Cronin and D. L. Cramer, *Nature*, 275 (1978)p. 744.
6. Ciochon and Corruccini (eds), *New Interpretations*, p. 691.
7. Susman (ed.), *The Pygmy Chimpanzee*. The description of pygmy chimp characteristics and behaviour given here comes mainly from that volume.
8. Susman (ed.), *The Pygmy Chimpanzee*, p. 411.
9. Lewin, *Human Evolution*, p. 21.
10. Susman (ed.), *The Pygmy Chimpanzee*, p. 417.

CHAPTER 2

1. For example, see Brophy and Wills, *Human Development*, p. 39.
2. Holloway describes his work in his contribution to the volume of *Scientific American* reprints called *Biological Anthropology*, published by W. H. Freeman in 1975. The quotes later are from that article. His work is put in context by Richard Leakey in *The Making of Mankind* and *Origins*.
3. Gribbin, *Future Weather*.

CHAPTER 3

1. Johanna Turner, *Cognitive Development*, in the 'Essential Psychology' series edited by Peter Herriott for Methuen, London. This particular volume was first published in 1975.
2. The best we know of is *Left Brain, Right Brain*, by Sally Springer and George Deutsch.
3. N. Toth, *Journal of Human Evolution*, 14 (1986) p. 607.
4. Quoted by Steve Turner, *New Society*, 26 July 1984, p. 17.

CHAPTER 4

1. E. O. Wilson, *New Scientist*, 13 May 1976, p. 344.
2. J. Krebs, 'Sociobiology ten years on', *New Scientist*, 3 October 1985, p. 40.
3. Steven Rose, Leon Kamin and R. C. Lewontin, *Not in Our Genes*, is a good example of this (false) line of argument.
4. Quotes from *Nature*, 19 July 1984, p. 255.

CHAPTER 5

1. Trivers *Social Evolution*, p. 81.
2. Trivers, *Social Evolution*, p. 47.
3. Discussed by Barash, *Sociobiology and Behavior*, p. 89, among others.
4. Wilson, *Sociobiology*, p. 58.

CHAPTER 6

1. Trivers, *Social Evolution*, p. 315.
2. Cherfas and Gribbin, *The Redundant Male*.
3. Barash, *Sociobiology and Behavior*, p. 214.
4. Daly and Wilson, *Sex, Evolution and Behavior*, p. 73.
5. Daly and Wilson, *Sex, Evolution and Behavior*, p. 75.
6. Wilson, *On Human Nature*, p. 132. The second quote is from the same source.

CHAPTER 7

1. Reported in John Crane (ed.), *Annual Editions: Biology*, Dushkin, Connecticut, 1984, p. 72.
2. Daly and Wilson, *Sex, Evolution and Behaviour*, p. 157.
3. For example, Trivers, *Social Evolution*, Chapter 12.
4. Trivers, *Social Evolution*, p. 332.

CHAPTER 8

1. Wilson, *On Human Nature*, p. 104.
2. Colinvaux, *The Fates of Nations*.
3. Colinvaux, *The Fates of Nations*, p. 223.
4. You can find details of this in B. Newmand and M. Dando (eds), *Nuclear Deterrence: Implications and Policy Options for the 1980s*, Castle House Press, London, 1982.

APPENDIX

1. Masami Hasegawa, Hirohisa Kishino and Taka-aki Yano, *Journal of Molecular Evolution*, 22 (1985), p. 160.

BIBLIOGRAPHY

Sources mentioned in the text, and other books we found interesting and relevant to the theme of our book, are cited fully here. Those marked with an asterisk are a little less accessible to the lay reader than the others, but all are worth following up if you have the time and inclination.

David Barash, *Sociobiology and Behavior*, 2nd edn, Elsevier, Amsterdam, 1982. Although this is a textbook, it is quite accessible to the lay reader (and does not require an asterisk!) and provides a very clear account of the basic principles of sociobiology. Trivers' book is even better to read, but Barash is more comprehensive and provides an invaluable detailed bibliography.

*Jere Brophy and Sherry Willis, *Human Development & Behaviour*, St Martin's Press, 1981.
A textbook for those who want to delve deeper into the subjects such as the nature/nurture controversy, social development, and so on. Not for the casual reader.

Arthur Caplan (ed.), *The Sociobiology Debate*, Harper & Row, 1978.
A collection of readings from both sides of the debate that raged during the middle 1970s. Now slightly out of date, but a useful historical guide, from which you can draw your own conclusions about who has the sounder scientific arguments.

Jeremy Cherfas and John Gribbin, *The Redundant Male*, Pantheon, New York, and Grafton, London, 1984.
A detailed look at human sex, making the case that men have outlived their evolutionary 'purpose'.

*Russell Ciochon and Robert Corruccini (eds), *New Interpretations of Ape and Human Ancestry*, Plenum, New York, 1983.
A weighty (888 pages) scientific tome which includes some fascinating and readable chapters on the molecular clock and on the pygmy chimpanzee. Worth digging out of a library.

Paul Colinvaux, *Why Big Fierce Animals are Rare*, Pelican, 1980.
An excellent, readable account of how the living world works.

Paul Colinvaux, *The Fates of Nations*, Pelican, 1983.
Slightly less accessible than *Why Big Fierce . . .*, and with a more 'serious', somewhat controversial message about historical imperatives, derived from the author's training in ecology. Thought-provoking perspective on humankind as an animal species.

*Helena Curtis, *Biology*, 2nd edn, Worth, New York, 1975.
Our favourite overview of biology, because it is the best. No less than 1065 pages, with something about anything you want to know about life, including the topics discussed in our book. There is a more recent edition – the one we have is therefore a little out of date, but still an old friend. For those with a serious interest, however.

Martin Daly and Margo Wilson, *Sex, Evolution and Behavior*, Duxbury Press, Massachusetts, 1978.
Perhaps just technical enough to merit half an asterisk, but the most definitive reasonably accessible account of what sex is all about.

Charles Darwin, *The Origin of Species* and *The Descent of Man*, Random House Modern Library.
Curiously, this modern reprint of both Darwin's classics in a single volume at an incredibly low price ($8.95 when we bought it in 1985) does not carry a publication date; however, the edition of the *Origin* is the sixth, from 1872, while the version of the *Descent* is the first, from 1871. The whole runs to exactly 1000 pages and includes Darwin's lengthy discussion of selection in relation to sex. He wrote beautifully, with great clarity, and anyone interested in evolution and human origins should find these originals fascinating.

The text of the first edition of the *Origin*, which in some ways presents Darwin's ideas most clearly, can be found in a Penguin edition, reprinted most recently in 1983.

Richard Dawkins, *The Extended Phenotype*, Oxford University Press Paperback, 1983 (original edition, W. H. Freeman, 1982).
A delicious book in which Dawkins, a superb writer, elaborates on the theme he developed originally in his more 'popular' account, *The Selfish Gene*. Taking on board, and responding to, the criticism that that book received, he has produced a book that is of major significance to professional biologists but also entirely intelligible, and enjoyable, for the interested onlooker. Probably the best, and most convincing, evidence in broad support of the ideas of human sociobiology.

Richard Dawkins, *The Blind Watchmaker*, Longman, 1986.
If *The Extended Phenotype* is the best presentation of the case for human sociobiology, *The Blind Watchmaker* is the best presentation of the case for evolution itself. Darwin would have loved it. Beautifully written, compelling and scientifically sound, it is well worth reading, even though the fact of evolution itself is not a major theme of our own book.

Kurt Fischer and Arlyne Lazerson, *Human Development*, Freeman, New York, 1984.
Marketed as a textbook, but completely intelligible to the intelligent lay person, clear and comprehensive. But more something to borrow from a library than one to burden your own bookshelves with permanently – 700+ large-format pages on everything from heredity to the problems of adolescence.

Stephen Jay Gould, *The Mismeasure of Man*, Pelican, London, 1984 (original edition, W. W. Norton, New York, 1981).
The best book we know of about the IQ 'debate'. As good a read as many a work of fiction, with astonishing insights into the way all too many scientists allowed their prejudices to influence their work. Unfortunately, in the final chapter of the book Gould allows his own prejudice against sociobiology to show through and cloud his judgement, but this does not affect his compelling history of the study of human intelligence.

John Gribbin, *Future Weather*, Delta, New York, and Pelican, London, 1982.
In spite of the title, this book contains a great deal on past weather, including the Ice Age/interglacial shifts that may have moulded human evolution.

John Gribbin, *In Search of the Double Helix*, Corgi, London, and McGraw-Hill, New York, 1985.

The story of evolution from Darwin, to DNA, and beyond into the modern understanding of genetics and the basis of life.

John Gribbin and Jeremy Cherfas, *The Monkey Puzzle*, Bodley Head, London, and Pantheon, New York, 1982.
Our own (human) family tree, with the emphasis on the techniques of molecular biology that show our very close relationship with the other African apes, and the significance of these findings.

Ernest Hilgard, Rita Atkinson and Richard Atkinson, *Introduction to Psychology*, 7th edn, Harcourt Brace Jovanovich, New York, 1979.
Known to generations of psychology students as 'Hilgard and Atkinson', with no mention of poor Richard, this is the undergraduate developmental psychologist's bible, and by no means inaccessible to the more casual reader who might want to dip into it in a library.

Donald C. Johanson and Maitland A. Edey, *Lucy*, Granada, London, 1981.
An exciting, highly readable account of the search for fossil remains in Ethiopia and of the discovery and interpretation of the fossils of 'Lucy', a human ancestor that lived three million years ago and looked very much like the preasent-day pygmy chimp. Johanson's pet theories on the mechanisms of evolution, and particularly the role of sex in human evolution, are, however, decidedly suspect and should be taken with a pinch of salt.

Richard Leakey, *The Making of Mankind*, Michael Joseph, London, 1981.
The book of the TV series in which master fossil hunter Leakey recounted the then accepted view of human origins.

Richard Leakey and Roger Lewin, *Origins*, Macdonald and Jane's, London, 1977.
The forerunner to Leakey's *Making of Mankind*, and a rather better book, even though it is slightly older and therefore a little out of date, and lacked the kudos of being tied to a major TV series. First class on language and intelligence, and worth reading simply for the chapter 'Aggression, sex and human nature'.

Roger Lewin, *Human Evolution*, Blackwell, London, 1984.
The best 'instant guide' to evolution and human origins, very clearly written in short chapters and with many excellent illustrations. Completely up to

date, with the molecular clock findings included, but no specific mention of *Pan paniscus*.

Elaine Morgan, *The Aquatic Ape*, Souvenir, London, 1984.
The theory that the selection pressures that turned an African ape into *Homo sapiens* may have owed much to a period of time spent by our ancestors on the shore of lake or ocean, finding food by diving. Very well written, although Morgan's dates for key events in human evolution are somewhat out of date – she does not take full account of the molecular evidence, although in fact the correct dating by no means invalidates her hypothesis. The argument is now receiving some attention from researchers studying human origins, having originally been dismissed as crazy.

*John Maynard Smith, *The Evolution of Sex*, Cambridge University Press, Cambridge, 1978.
It seems that 1978 was a good year for books about the evolution of sex, but this one is much more mathematically technical, and less readable, than Daly and Wilson's effort.

*John Maynard Smith, *Evolution and the Theory of Games*, Cambridge University Press, Cambridge, 1982.
The definitive study which establishes the mathematical foundations of the evolutionarily stable strategy idea. Mostly rather technical.

Sally Springer and Georg Deutsch, *Left Brain, Right Brain*, W. H. Freeman, New York, 1981.
We once planned to write a book about left-handedness, but changed our minds when we read this one and realized that we could never hope to improve on it. The best book we know of about the two brains that lie within each human skull, slightly 'academic' in tone but very accessible.

*Randall Susman, *The Pygmy Chimpanzee*, Plenum, New York, 1984.
The definitive, up-to-date nitty-gritty on *Pan paniscus*. But mostly rather heavy going; not for the faint hearted.

Robert Trivers, *Social Evolution*, Benjamin/Cummings, 1985.
More of a personal view than Barash's textbook, focusing on topics of special interest to Trivers, but a well-written and fascinating account of socio-biological ideas from a researcher who provided some of the key ideas in the 1970s. The best up-to-date account we know of.

Edward Wilson, *On Human Nature*, Harvard University Press, 1978.
An accessible account of the application of sociobiology to people.

Edward Wilson, *Sociobiology*, abridged edition, Havard University Press, 1980.
Even the abridged edition of Wilson's major work runs to 366 large-format pages of sometimes highly technical argument, and only the last chapter specifically discusses human sociobiology. But, like Darwin's books, anyone interested in our own origins will find this book enthralling, as well as essential, reading.

INDEX

adolescence 45–7, 85, 169–71
  see also children
advertising 80–2
aggression
  animal 176–7, 178
  human 91–2, 109–10, 123, 175ff
altruism 110–11, 114–16, 117–28, 173–4,
  185–7
ants, sociobiology of 140
australopithicenes 47–8, 50, 65–6, 189ff

babies, human 37–41, 57–8, 159ff
bases, molecular 9–10, 15
bees, sociobiology of 117–19
behaviour, social *see* sociobiology
Binet test 102–5
birds, sociobiology of 120–2, 146–7, 167
bonding, parent–child 159–63
brain, the
  abilities and 62–5, 75–80
  language-learning and 62–5
  music and 75–6
  quality of 48–9
  sizes of 34–5, 39, 47–51, 54, 101, 199
  structure of 49, 62–5, 77
  see also intelligence

children
  development of 40–4
  incest and 151

intelligence-testing of 102–5
  language and 58–61
  parent-bonding and 159–63
  relatedness of 115, 164
  see also adolescence; babies; parents
chimpanzees 5–8, 15–16, 21–4, 35, 168,
  172, 189ff
Chomsky, Noam 44, 61
chromosomes 9–12, 15ff
cognition, development of 42–4, 46
conflict, parent–offspring 163–73
Coolidge, Harold 5–7

Darwin, Charles 7, 117
deer, sociobiology of 143–4
disease 134–5
DNA 8–20, 94–5
Dryopithecus 191ff

education 44
  intelligence-testing and 102–5
  left-handedness and 69–70
  sexual equality and 157–8
embryos, development of human 29–32
environment
  child development and 40–2
  human evolution and 50–5, 100
  modification of 27
ESS (= evolutionarily stable strategy) 70–
  5, 94, 112–13, 120, 139–40, 185

evolution
  human 6–8, 14–24, 65–75, 99–100,
    114–16, 122–8, 133ff, 189–99
  process of 16–20, 27–9, 94–8, 109–13,
    111–22, 131ff
  see also altruism; ESS; genes; tit-for-tat,
    strategy of

family unit 137–8, 140–1, 147–53
foetuses, development of human 32–4

games theory
  evolution and 71–3, 94
  nuclear weapons and 182–4
genes 11–16, 26–8, 34, 69, 94–6, 111, 114–
    16, 139ff, 160ff
  see also evolution
gibbons 192ff
gorillas 5, 35, 190ff

helix, double see DNA
Homo erectus 48, 50, 65, 190
Homo habilis 48, 49, 65–6, 68–9, 190
Homo sapiens neanderthalis 48
Homo sapiens sapiens
  adolescence of 45–7, 85, 169–71
  aggression in 91–2, 109–10, 123, 175ff
  altruism of 110–11, 114–16, 122–8,
    173–4, 185–7
  babies of 37–41, 57–8, 159ff
  brains of 34–5, 39, 47–51, 54, 62–5, 75–
    80, 101, 199
  children of 40–5, 58–61, 102–5, 115,
    151, 159–64
  embryo development of 29–32
  environmental change and 27, 50–5,
    100
  evolution of 6–8, 14–24, 65–75, 99–
    100, 114–16, 122–8, 133ff, 189–99
  foetus development of 32–4
  incest by 150–1
  intelligence of 98–107
  language-learning by 44–5, 57–65,
    85–6
  puberty of 45–6

reproduction of 131–41, 147–58
sociobiology of 109–16, 122–8, 133,
  136–42, 147–58
tool-use by 66ff
see also left-handedness; marriage;
  parents; population; right-
  handedness
homosexuality 156

incest 150–1
intelligence 98–107, 126

language, learning of 44–5, 57–65, 85–6
left-handedness 67–70, 73–5, 76–80
lions, sociobiology of 144–5
'Lucy' 21–2, 189ff

mankind see Homo sapiens sapiens
marriage 149–54
monogamy 140ff
music 75–6, 80–5

neoteny 36–7, 47
niches, ecological 180
nuclear arms race 182–7

orang-utans 191ff

Pan paniscus 5–8, 20, 21–4
parents
  child-bonding and 159–63
  offspring-conflict and 163–73
  step- 171–2
phenotypes, definition of 16
Piaget, Jean 42–4, 46, 57
polyandry 149
polygamy 140ff
polygyny 142ff
population, growth of 179–82
predators 176–7
proteins 14–19
puberty 45–6

Ramapithecus 190ff
ratios, sex 138–40

relatedness 115–16, 118–22, 140, 164
reproduction
    bio-chemistry of 10–14
    sexual 131–58
right-handedness 67–70, 76–80
roles, sex 136–40, 141–8, 154–8

seals, sociobiology of 145–6
selection, natural *see* evolution
sex *see* reproduction, sexual
sex ratios *see* ratios
sex roles *see* roles
smiling 161
sociobiology
    intelligence and 98–107

of *Homo sapiens sapiens* 109–16, 122–8,
    133, 136–42, 147–58
of other species 116–22, 140, 142–7,
    167
value and scope of 89–98
species, definition of 26–7
survival, strategies of 71–3
    see also altruism; evolution; games
        theory; tit-for-tat

tit-for-tat, strategy of 185–7
tools, use of 66ff

warfare 179, 182